CORPORATE MANAGEMENT IN CRISIS:

Why the Mighty Fall

CORPORATE MANAGEMENT IN CRISIS:

Why the Mighty Fall

Joel E. Ross

Michael J. Kami

PRENTICE-HALL, INC.   *ENGLEWOOD CLIFFS, N.J.*

PRENTICE-HALL INTERNATIONAL, INC., *London*
PRENTICE-HALL OF AUSTRALIA, PTY. LTD., *Sydney*
PRENTICE-HALL OF CANADA, LTD., *Toronto*
PRENTICE-HALL OF INDIA PRIVATE LTD., *New Delhi*
PRENTICE-HALL OF JAPAN, INC., *Tokyo*

Library of Congress Cataloging in Publication Data

Ross, Joel E
    Corporate management in crisis.

    1. Industrial management--United States--Case studies.
2. Big business--United States--Case studies. I. Kami,
Michael J., 1922-   joint author. II. Title.
HD70.U5R66   658.4   73-6574

Printed in the United States of America

HOW TO BENEFIT FROM THE
MISTAKES THE MIGHTY MAKE

How is it possible that so many companies with billions of dollars of resources and established records of accomplishment, with images of "national institutions" and the power to hire the best possible talent in the world, have declined precipitously in their performance? We cannot accept the excuses of excessive size or uncontrollable external factors. Fluctuations and changes in our economy, union pressures, changing consumer demands, increasing costs, deteriorating morale or government legislation are part of doing business and running a company. The blame for any failure can be only attributed to faulty management, unprepared for or unconcerned with change.

The purpose of analyzing a few companies among the giants and trying to find a common thread of management mistakes was not to condemn them or help them, but to learn from the mistakes of the mighty in order to help the small and the medium-size businesses in the United States, upon which our economic system was established, and which still form the foundation of our society. But these smaller concerns are and will be in increasing management trouble.

The complexity of society, the rapid change and cost of technology, the increasing rate of product and service obsolescence makes management of smaller businesses far more difficult than management of giants, because of the obvious shortage of resources, both financial and human.

If executives of these enterprises could profit by avoiding some mistakes that have hit the large corporations, then the purpose of

5

the authors will have been accomplished. The interested reader should put himself in an objective frame of mind and while reading the book should jot down how many of the items discussed can also affect him and his company. He should ask himself, "Am I making the same errors?"

One of the authors discussed the 18 holes of management golf (18 potential trouble spots) with an audience of businessmen. He noticed that one of the participants was smiling and chuckling throughout the presentation. After the lecture the businessman was asked what was so funny. He replied, "I run a very small company. In a few years I managed to make 15 out of the 18 mistakes you described—at least I am in good company!"

The key question is, however: What will he do tomorrow and the day after to correct the management errors he has recognized?

An important factor in using the book for practical purposes is to realize the specificity of the general statements and not to consider them platitudes or a "firm grasp of the obvious." Rapid change and, conversely, "slow reaction to change" may be obvious, general and well known, but this does not mean that it does not create specific and precise negative consequences which could and should be corrected by different styles of managing, by different actions, by different policies and different decisions of management.

Another point to remember is that time moves on. The reader may find that Chrysler and others may be back on the road to recovery or that the continuing saga of PanAm or Lockheed has new facets not covered in this book. This fact alone shows the tremendous amount of change that can occur in a company in a period of a few months.

But the basic lessons are considered valid because they *are* basic and conceptual rather than topical or opportunistic. They apply, in the opinion of the authors, to companies small or large and to every classification of the industrial and service sector.

Obviously the book is not all-inclusive. Many other examples could have been chosen. Perhaps other additional conclusions could have been drawn. The authors have attempted to select what in their judgment were the key points to examine and watch. A businessman in any size of enterprise who will seriously analyze and audit his operations, trying to avoid the pitfalls described here, may well be on his way to profitable growth as against the too many who are rapidly sliding in a downhill loss spiral, a spiral increasingly difficult to reverse.

The organization of the book is straightforward. First, we define the nature of the crisis in management and demonstrate how selected companies in a number of industries (e.g., aerospace, airlines, computers, retailing, etc.) have managed to mismanage their affairs. The errors and omissions of some of our largest companies—and managers—will surprise you.

Second, we treat our basic list of management fundamentals in some depth for the purpose of showing the manager how he can improve his performance and the results of his company. Illustrations, suggestions, and summaries are provided throughout so that the reader can rapidly recall the "do's and don'ts" of good management.

Finally, we include a comprehensive summary or check-off list so that the reader can perform a self audit on the management of his own company. We call this "Handicap Your Company's Management." We hope it will be of help to you.

Food for thought: In January 1963, *Dun's Review* conducted a poll among 300 chief executives of large corporations asking them to select the ten best-managed companies in the country. Today only four of them—household words in industry—are in positions of undisputed leadership. Four would probably be dropped without any hesitation and we would probably consider eliminating the two remaining because new and better leaders have emerged. This book tells what went wrong and why. And it offers solid guidance for *any* company that wants to avoid the pitfalls of the mighty.

Joel E. Ross
Michael J. Kami

CONTENTS

5. Computers: Snow White and the Seven Dwarfs *(cont.)*

6. Conglomerates: Synergism at LTV Makes 2+2=3 82

7. Autos: Is There a Chrysler in Big Three's Future 91

7. Autos: Is There a Chrysler in Big Three's Future *(cont.)*

8. Whatever Happened to the Great A&P 102

Part II CAUSES AND CURES

9. AT&T's Wrong Number 117

13. Board of Directors: Rubber Stamps? *(cont.)*

14. One-Man Rule: The Shadow of the Leader Is Shortening Fast 168

15. Slow Reaction to Change: You Can't Plan the Future on the Past 177

16. Consumerism: The Customer Is King 190

17. Computers: Use But Don't Misuse *(cont.)*

18. Accounting Manipulations: You Can't Fool Everybody for Long 219

19. Organization: The Structure of the Sixties Doesn't Fit the Needs for the Seventies 233

Part III CHECK YOUR OWN PERFORMANCE

Part I
The Companies and the Crisis

Chapter 1

THE CRISIS IN MANAGEMENT: ITS CAUSES

We are faced with a management crisis!

The top 500 industrial corporations in the United States account for more than 65 percent of corporate sales and 75 percent of profits. Despite the tremendous advances these companies have made in science and technology, and the economic power they can muster, many of their managements are woefully behind. Unless rapid improvements in management techniques are made, increasing failures and decreasing productivity will result.

During the past ten years a large number of big and powerful corporations have experienced rapid and unforseen reverses. These downfalls were not precipitated by technological breakthroughs or spectacular market shifts, but by various management errors that were committed in the normal course of established operations. The problem was summarized by J. Irwin Miller, president of Cummins: "I think we've just gone through a decade of rather surprisingly *bad* decisions by businessmen worldwide. Some of them so bad that nobody would have guessed it."

How much more can the stockholders, the public and the government take?

The bad guys and the good guys

Consider the fate of some of our most famous billion-dollar giants: AT&T, A&P, General Dynamics, Litton, Lockheed,

Chrysler, Penn Central, and many others. All of these companies could afford to develop or buy the best available management talent in the world. Yet they managed to *mismanage* their affairs, squander the profits of stockholders, and in general act in a manner somewhat less than responsible during the recent past.

The nature of this *crisis in management* can be highlighted by comparing some of the poorly managed companies (bad guys) with their competitors (good guys) or a related firm in the same or similar industry.

BAD GUY	GOOD GUY
A &P. Trying to recover from "ten year sleep" and hardening of corporate arteries."	*J. C. Penney's.* Made a turnaround by commitment to new strategy and infusion of better management. Return on equity is highest in the business.
Chrysler. This "up and down" yo-yo company is trying to regain markets, public confidence, liquidity and profits that have eroded through sudden bad management.	*Ford.* Is fast on its wheels and does most of the right things. *Inside* they practice the basic fundamentals of management and *outside* they keep on top of changing customer needs and desires.
Ling-Temco-Vought. Former "darling of conglomerates" can't pay interest on $700 million debt. Jim Ling, "Sweetheart of Wall Street," ousted.	*IT&T.* Hard-driving Harold Geneen keeps this conglomerate on top of the heap by adopting sound strategy for planned growth. Understands and practices *synergism.*
Lockheed. Flying down the road that was followed by Krupp, Rolls-Royce and Penn Central.	*United Aircraft.* Head and shoulders above the crowd in aerospace. Avoided "high flying" management so common in the industry.
Penn Central. Bankrupt!	*Union Pacific.* That's the way to run a railroad.
20th Century Fox. $114 million loss in two years due to the charismatic but autocratic, Darryl Zanuck, who had almost total lack of management concepts.	*Walt Disney.* A well-managed operation that always knew what the American public wanted and gave it to them. Strategy of growth in a business they knew best.

BAD GUY	GOOD GUY
Pan American. Growing deficit for three consecutive years.	*Delta.* Consistent money maker. Best managed of major airlines.
RCA. One of the "seven dwarfs" in computer industry lost in the fight for leftover market of "Snow White" (IBM). Over $400 million down the drain.	*IBM.* Ranked #1 in market value in U.S. Outstanding success story of how good strategy pays off.
AT&T. Trying to regain public support after degrading of its only product—customer service.	No comparable company.

Why the crisis?

By and large these corporate managers have either overlooked or failed to comply with some rather "classic" or basic principles of management. For simplicity, let's call them:

THE TEN COMMANDMENTS OF MANAGEMENT

  I   Develop and communicate a *strategy* . . . a *unified sense of direction* to which all members of the organization can relate.

 II   If you want to achieve plans, programs, and policies, then *overall controls* and *cost controls* must be established.

III   Exercise care in the selection of a *Board of Directors* and require that they actively *participate in management.*

IV   Avoid *one-man rule.*

  V   Provide *management depth.*

VI   Keep informed of change and *react to change.*

VII   Don't overlook the customer and the *customer's new power.*

VIII   Use but don't misuse computers.

 IX   Do not engage in *accounting manipulations.*

  X   Provide for an *organizational structure* that meets the *need of people.*

Let's see how the failure to observe these *Ten Commandments of Management* has contributed to a *crisis in management* in selected "bad guy" companies:

Strategy

To develop and communicate a *strategy,* a *unified sense of direction* to which all members of the organization can relate, is probably the most important concept in management for top level consideration, and yet it is frequently overlooked. Unless the organization—its people and management—have an objective—a corporate identity—a philosophy of what you are in business for—and some plans to achieve these objectives—then there is no unified direction that management can use to relate day to day decisions. And to employees the company will become just a place to work.

Without a *strategy* the organization is like a ship without a rudder, going around in circles. It's like a tramp; it has no place to go. And incidentally, such platitudes as "make a profit" or "increase market share" do *NOT* provide the *unified direction* we are seeking.

IBM and the computer industry provides us with a good example of how *strategy* can pay off. IBM has attained its growth and its embarrassingly large share of the market by the systematic introduction of new generations of computers and office equipment. The strategy behind this growth has been their intentional development of each specific end-use market. Moreover, they have not only developed new computers but have also concentrated on the appropriate software for the problem of individual industry-users. Thus, IBM has not only expanded its market by attention to developing needs, but its prominent position has also been attained by building a reputation for servicing the "hardware" that it manufactures.

This successful *strategy* was recently highlighted by the comment of a Director of Management Information Systems for a major corporation:

> "There's not that much difference between computers. But when you buy one from . . . (CDC, Honeywell, RCA, Univac, GE, NCR, etc.) . . . they bolt it to the floor and that's the last you see of them. On the other hand, IBM is as close as the nearest telephone if I have trouble."

Incidentally, Lockheed's two-part strategy: (a) Let defense contracts pay for R&D, and (b) Let defense contracts carry the lion's share of the business . . . seems, in retrospect, to have been ill-chosen.

Controls

Another fundamental is that if you want to achieve plans, programs, and policies, then *overall controls* and *cost controls* must be established.

A classic case of failure to obey this elementary principle of management is provided by *Lockheed Aircraft.* For nine of the ten years during the decade 1960-70, this company was the nation's leading defense contractor. But look at the recent record: Earnings plunged from a profit of $58.9 million in 1966 to a loss of $86.3 million in 1970. Because the failure of this company is so closely tied to the national security and economic well-being of the country, its management crisis may very well set a new milestone in corporate vis-à-vis government relations. And like any giant company, its sins could have dire consequences on other firms doing business with it. In other words, failure has a "multiplier effect."

Although the causes for Lockheed's *crisis* are complex, one fact stands out—management failed to maintain *overall control* of general corporate performance (including technology) and specifically, they failed to maintain *cost control* of tremendous contract cost overruns. It appears that the company forgot the elementary steps in *control:*

(1) Set standards of performance.
(2) Measure performance against this standard.
(3) Correct deviations from standard.

There is also some evidence that Lockheed, like so many technology companies, was run *by* engineers *for* engineers and hence engineering considerations overcame good management considerations. Among these was the failure to maintain *control.*

The Board

The *Board of Directors* presents a peculiar dichotomy of American industry. On the one hand you have the legal requirement (reinforced by custom and tradition) for a board of directors, and on the other hand you have the rather obvious situation where most boards are little more than ineffective window dressing.

The situation has been glossed over for many years, but it took the Penn Central "incident" to focus attention upon it. No less than three dozen suits have been filed by disgruntled Penn Central shareholders seeking to prove that the duties of prudence and loyalty were somewhat less than diligently pursued, if not abandoned altogether. On the eve of bankruptcy, Penn Central reported $4.4 million profit in 1969, while their actual loss was $122 million. The situation was further compounded by the continued payment of a high rate of dividends despite a negative cash flow! The question arises: Was the board of directors wearing blinders, or was it simply not involved?

The real problem is that most boards are "rubber stamps" for the chief executive. The reasons for this are many but generally can be summarized:

    (1) No one really agrees on what a board should do.

    (2) The role of the board is whatever the chief executive makes it, and it is a rare chief executive who wants "interference" from a strong board.

    (3) The board doesn't look after the interest of the shareholder or the public.

    (4) The board members, "see, hear, and speak no evil" of the companies on whose boards they sit.

    (5) Boards simply don't have the time and interest to be well informed about the company.

    (6) Boards are looked upon as ornaments on the corporate Christmas tree.

This sorry state of affairs can be illustrated again in the case of Chrysler—a company whose record and results reflect the violation of a number of good management practices.

In the case of Chrysler and its board of directors, it became evident some time ago that they were a "rubber stamp" for Chairman Lynn Townsend. Although this exceptionally capable executive was largely responsible for the turnaround in Chrysler during the period 1960-68, he ultimately became overconfident and involved in several serious errors of managerial judgment. These costly errors were probably due, in part, to the free hand given Townsend by a board of directors that considered his management team "great" and Townsend himself as "infallible."

The question arises: Would not the relatively poor results at Chrysler have been much better if the board had participated more closely in the management of the company?

One-man rule

The fourth commandment: *Avoid one-man rule* . . . follows naturally from the "rubber stamp board." However, the *one-man rule* goes a step further. The manager who practices this approach neither solicits nor will he accept help from anyone—board or subordinates.

Now we don't mean to deprecate the role of the strong leader. Indeed, some of our greatest success stories came from the "long shadow" of the capable chief executive—Walt Disney, Tom Watson of IBM, David Sarnoff of RCA, Harold Geneen of IT&T. On the other hand, consider those giant American corporations whose *crises* can be traced partially to *one-man rule:*

Jim Ling	of	Ling-Temco-Vought
Bernie Cornfeld	of	I.O.S.
Darryl Zanuck	of	20th Century Fox
Saunders	of	Penn Central

Generally speaking, *one-man rule* is bad news! Although the strong capable leader has served his purpose in the past and may do so in the future, it is the rare company that can prosper *in the long run* with *one-man rule*. In the extraordinarily complex organizations of the 1970's and 1980's, it is essential to have management depth and permit them to participate in decision making. This corporate attribute is necessary for two reasons: first, one man simply cannot handle the complexity of running the organization single handed, and second, it is essential that the company provide for management depth.

Management depth

It is no coincidence that year after year the President's Panel of *Dun's Review and Modern Industry* identifies management depth as of the prime characteristics of its "Ten Best Managed Companies" in the United States. Year after year such blue-chip companies as Ford, Avon, Procter & Gamble, 3M, IBM, and Sears are identified as *"well managed"* because of their careful attention to bench strength in management. With these companies it is a corporate way of life.

If, on the other hand, we take the "not so well managed companies"—those whose sales, earnings, and P/E ratios have fallen or fluctuated drastically—we find that a common characteristic is lack of management depth. Sometimes this lack has been due to one-man rule and sometimes to rapid growth due to acquisition and merger. At any rate, the "bench strength" has not been available to handle the expansion in size or complexity. Consider such diverse industries as aerospace (Lockheed), motion pictures (20th Century Fox), transportation (Penn Central), conglomerates (Litton), retailing (A & P), and finance (I.O.S.).

Although the sorry record of these companies is not attributable solely to lack of management depth, it is safe to say that their recent downhill slide can be traced partly to violation of this fundamental principle. Moreover, it is a sure bet that many, if not most, of their difficulties would have been averted if they had made the necessary plans to provide for good managers in appropriate numbers.

Capable managers represent the greatest asset of any company, and it pays to have the very best. By and large, this means internal development rather than pirating from others. Changes in the economy, growth, new products, accelerating technology, and complexity are among those factors limiting the supply of good managers. If the successful firm is to achieve its objective(s), it must provide for the necessary management talent.

React to change

Lack of *reaction to change* has been a serious cause of a *management crisis.* We are not talking of those familiar product changes that are so spectacular, such as the car vs. the horse and buggy or xerography vs. wet duplicating, but with those more subtle, yet evident changes that managers must be on top of.

Recall Chrysler's too-late and costly reaction to the mini car. Consider the inertia of the motion picture industry (eg. MGM and 20th Century Fox) to the change in taste of the movie-going public. It is interesting to note that while the giants were losing millions on extravaganzas like "Hello Dolly," Disney was inexorably improving earnings with such "unspectacular" family fare as a movie about a Volkswagen called "The Lovebug."

Another illustration is that of the giant A&P which completely missed the boat by not reacting in time to the change in consumer spending patterns that make the supermarket the center of activity in the suburban shopping center.

The customer

The admonition to *react to change* is directly connected with the seventh commandment: *Don't Overlook the Customer!* Indeed, change is usually caused by some reaction on the part of the customer. In the 1970's, more than ever before, the customer has a *new power* and is more demanding than ever. *Nader did not create consumerism; consumerism created Nader.*

We have had historic cases of the non-perpetuity of some large corporations due to "marketing myopia"—non-perception of fundamental changes in technology and basic shifts in customer demand. However, in the seventies and eighties perception must be much more rapid. Moreover, the customer has a *new* power—the power to make or break the corporation.

Let's briefly recall a few near failures caused in part by *overlooking the customer:*

(1) A&P, which has suffered from "hardening of the corporate arteries" in the last decade, continues to pursue a losing marketing strategy based on the price differential of its house brands . . . a strategy about which the customer could care very little.

(2) AT&T, also suffering from the same "hardening" as A&P, faces a critical situation brought on by a tidal wave of public non-confidence resulting from a downgrading of the quality of AT&T's only product—customer service.

(3) Union Carbide, which "fired" its chief executive because customer power had labeled the firm "America's Worst Polluter."

Consider, on the other hand, some better managed companies that *did not overlook the customer:*

(1) Disney, a firm that has always had its hand on the pulse of the movie-goer, now reacts to customer trends directed to tourism in the U.S. and its resultant affinity to visitations to natural sites (e.g., Disneyland, California, and Disney World, Florida).

(2) President Bon Dix of Continental Airlines initiates "flight frills" that capture customers and improve seat occupancy while other airlines languish.

(3) Harold Geneen of IT&T incorporates customer and public demand for corporate social responsibility into marketing strategy and advertising (e.g., ecology, etc.).

There is no doubt about it! The customer and the public have a new power. This power can make or break the company that depends upon the public for sales. Moreover, this power will grow in the socially conscious seventies, and it is a wise management—a socially conscious management—a marketing oriented management—that takes account of it.

Computers

Can *misuse of computers* be really a contributing factor to a major management crisis? You bet your company it can!

Admit that the primary job of managers is to make decisions. Admit further that decisions are made (or should be made) based upon information. Now, if we assume (as we must) that computer-based information systems exist for the purpose of providing information to decision makers, then we can begin to see the consequences of poorly designed and improperly used management information systems (MIS).

In addition to their importance in the management process, computers have the potential for disaster if used incorrectly in the area of clerical applications as well. Some classic boners would be very funny if they weren't so costly:

(1) Between 450 and 650 boxcars operated by Penn Central were either lost or stolen due to faulty routing and reporting by the company's computer.

(2) At a stockholders' meeting, Gimbel Brothers reported a raise in their provision for doubtful accounts from $9

million to $15 million and gave as their reason, "$6 million has gone uncollected in the New York Store alone due to computer problems."

(3) In 1968 Lynn Townsend's famous computer system broke down at Chrysler. The results included wrong schedules, delay in deliveries, and the shipment of thousands of cars to wrong destinations.

Those managers who are interested in the *use* and not the *misuse* of computers might follow the lead of such well-managed companies as Westinghouse, Weyerhaeuser, and Pillsbury.

Accounting manipulations

Accounting manipulations can easily contribute to a *management crisis.*

No well-managed company would engage in widespread accounting manipulations—particularly for the purpose of bamboozling the public. Among the bad effects such practice might cause are: (a) management might be lulled to sleep in the mistaken belief that *figures* represent *fact,* (b) a mistaken belief that certain figures (eg., inventory) represent *cash,* whereas these figures may be vastly overstated or incorrect, and (c) the establishment of a bad precedent and the danger of promoting a climate of manipulation.

Let's consider three recent cases of accounting manipulation and the results:

(1) In an effort to cover up impending doom, the management of Penn Central engaged in several instances of near fraud. Among these manipulations was the continued payment of high dividends while simultaneously losing enormous sums of money. In 1968-69 over $100 million in dividends were paid despite the fact that the company had a negative cash flow in both years.

(2) Jim Ling admitted that during the acquisition binge of Ling-Temco-Vought during the middle and late sixties, his only criterion was the price of his stock. To achieve these high prices he had a strategy that he called "redeployment of assets." Others called his acquisition of the stock of acquired

companies "funny money" and others "castro pesos." These labels referred, of course, to the inflated price of LTV stock. Finally, the accounting manipulations caught up with Ling. Among the results are a stock price drop from 169 to 7 and a debt situation of $700 million, including an inability to cover interest charges.

Organization

The *last commandment of management concerns organization and people.* It's obvious that no organization can function without *people.* We can have the best management, money, machines, facilities and products, but *people must make the organization go.*

All management authorities are generally in agreement that our major concern in the 1970's and 80's must be with *people* and how we can release the enormous latent potential for creativity and productivity that exists in all of us. We are concerned with organization *structure* and setting a *climate for motivation.*

The *structure* can range from the extremes of the old classical and authoritative Theory X to the more recent permissive Theory Y approach. However, whatever the structure that provides for coordination of work specialization, a motivational climate must be set—and this involves building an organization that meets the needs of its members.

To illustrate, take the case of how a great American corporation permitted "hardening of corporate arteries" to precipitate a loss of public confidence. AT&T is now faced with widespread criticism and accusations of "the public be damned" attitude against their management. Why? Well, to oversimplify, it was a case of failure to change organization *structure* (including policies) to accommodate people.

A major facet of the situation can be traced to AT&T's insistence on an historical system of standardized operations—everything is written, explained, and programmed in procedures—Bell System Practices (BSP's) are super-complete. This *rigidity* (including in-breeding of management talent) led to an *impersonal* climate, which in turn led to turnover and loss of efficiency and productivity. Policies that may have worked very well in the past were not changed to accommodate changing conditions.

LESSONS TO BE LEARNED

It is interesting to note that all of the companies in which a *crisis in management* exists are guilty of violating *most* of the commandments of management. To put it another way—the causes for crisis are practically the same in all companies. Although all companies are not guilty of permitting *all causes for crisis*, their degree of success/failure is a function of how well they manage according to the *ten commandments of management*. The similarity between causes and companies is summarized below. We will be concerned in the remainder of the book with these and other companies, more details concerning their relative success/failure and its *causes*, but more specifically—*THE CURES!!*

Commandment of Management	A&P	AT&T	Chrysler	Ling-Temco-Vought	Lockheed	Penn Central	Rolls Royce	20th Century Fox
STRATEGY	X	X	X	X	X	X	X	X
CONTROLS	X	X	X	X	X	X	X	X
BOARD OF DIRECTORS	X	X	X	X	X	X		X
ONE-MAN RULE			X	X	X	X	X	X
MANAGEMENT DEPTH	X			X		X	X	X
REACTION TO CHANGE	X	X	X	X	X	X	X	X
CUSTOMER	X	X	X	X	X	X		X
ACCOUNTING			X	X	X	X	X	X
ORGANIZATION	X	X	X	X	X	X	X	X
COMPUTERS	X			X	X		X	

Chapter 2

AEROSPACE: FLYING LOW
AT LOCKHEED AND ROLLS-ROYCE

"On these fixed-price contracts with the
Government, you can be doing $500 million
in sales and lose your butt."
W.L. (Bill) Gore, Senior VP
Aerojet-General

In 1968 a Pentagon cost-efficiency expert named Ernest Fitz-
gerald startled his Pentagon superiors and Congress, as well as the
management of Lockheed, with the news of actual and impending
huge cost overruns on the company's contract to build 115 C5
supertransport planes for the Air Force. These overruns would
eventually exceed $2 billion and have ripple effects throughout
the country.

While cost and time overruns were nothing new to the Defense
Department and to a lesser extent the general business community, the ordinary citizen was not aware of such manipulations
with his tax dollar. However, the taxpayer shouldn't have been too
surprised. The Lockheed case was merely a larger example of the
typical homeowner whose exposure to contracting ends with
giving a tradesman the go-ahead for a new roof or paint job on the
house, and finding later that there is an "overrun." Thus, to the
public at large the aerospace industry—yesterday's heroes—became
the scapegoat for public opinion that turned perceptibly and
inexorably away from big spending for defense and space.

The aerospace and defense industry was indeed troubled as it embarked on the early years of the seventies. Rolls-Royce was bankrupt. Only a last minute congressional loan guarantee had kept Lockheed from a similar fate. It is doubtful whether Douglas Aircraft would have survived if it were not for a merger with McDonnel. Boeing was in trouble and only the non-defense business of General Dynamics kept it off the rocks.

Spectacular failures included the TFX (F-111) fighter plane at General Dynamics, the C5A transport plane (airbus) at Lockheed, and the SST at Boeing.

The problem is management

What goes on? What is the problem in the industry?

There is little doubt that the top management of the aerospace and defense industry would tend to blame the combination of inflation, reduction of defense expenditures, and the winding down of the Vietnam War. And add to this the very nature of doing business in aerospace. There is also common tendency to explain away difficulties due to the nature of the product involved. Because design and production were so sophisticated it was said that the contractor must first *invent* the product before building it. This, in turn, led to a large number of unknowns (labeled "unks unks") in advanced technology that can't be anticipated because there is no way of knowing that they will be problems.

Although the industry had more than its share of complexity and unknowns, the *real* problem lay in management—the bread and butter principles of planning, organizing, and controlling that we have outlined. During decades of "cost plus" and "renegotiated" defense procurement, contractors had become sloppy and complacent once a contract had been landed. President Wilson of Boeing admitted the company had accumulated considerable fat during former prosperity and pruning was relatively easy, at least in the early stages after the SST debacle. In other words, managers had never been required to cope with strict cost-price-schedule relationships and consequently had become "fat, dumb, and happy." Defense Secretary McNamara's "total package procurement" concept was to change all this and contribute directly to the lean and hungry years.

Lockheed and the airbus

Item: In March, 1967, *Fortune Magazine* reported: "Lockheed has a major contender for the commercial 'jumbo jet' market in the C5A... With a pocketful of cash from a $125 million debenture issue, President Haughton will have little trouble in moving Lockheed ahead quickly." *Little did they know!*

Item: The week of February 13, 1971, was a week to remember at Lockheed. In these few days it accepted a $200 million loss settlement on a Pentagon contract to build the C5A transport, it received the news and shock of the bankruptcy of Rolls-Royce, which was to supply engines for its Tri-Star airbus (L-1011), and in a final blow—saw its main plant at Burbank rocked by an earthquake!

Item: On September 29, 1971, an Air Force pilot at Altus Air Force Base, Oklahoma, gave Lockheed's C5A a full throttle in a pre-flight check. The left outboard engine and mounting pylon tore off, spun 300 feet into the air and slammed onto the concrete runway in a flaming heap of metal. This led to the grounding of the Air Force's fleet of 47 shiny new C5A's while inspectors scoured them with x-rays, to determine whether any more engines were likely to fall off, or if the landing gear would work, or if additional wings could crack.

The problems of the nation's largest defense contractor can be traced back to 1959 when its Electra Turboprop (Lockheed made the tragic marketing mistake of assuming that full jet airliners were a long way off) began to fall apart in the skies. The plane's defects were corrected at a cost to Lockheed of $25 million, but the eventual sale of less than half of the 400 that had been forecasted resulted in a write-off of $250 million.

During the years following the Electra debacle, Lockheed patiently waited for a chance to get back into commercial airliners in a big way. Meanwhile they turned their attention to other defense projects and soon more than 90 percent of their business was derived from that source.

The opportunity to re-enter the commercial market was not long in coming. In 1964 the giants of the aircraft industry began competition for the $2 billion C-5 jet transport contract. The competition, generating no less than thirty-five *tons* of documents, was exhausting. The competitors: Lockheed, Boeing and Douglas for the airframe—General Electric and Pratt and Whitney for the engines—spent some $60 million of their own funds and assigned more than 4,000 top engineers to the undertaking. Why so much interest? Because the eventual payoff was to be much greater than the $2 billion contract, the winner could get a corner on a commercial market estimated at over *$15 billion.*

Lockheed won! It was the first of the Defense Department's *"fixed price"* contracts and called for 115 planes at a total cost of $1.9 billion. This bid was $400 million below Boeing's bid and $100 million under Douglas (later forced to merge with McDonnel). Did Lockheed "buy in?"

Despite a reputation for "buying in" to defense contracts, Lockheed denied this intent for the C-5. However, the stakes were big and Lockheed went after them in their characteristic tradition of fierce competition and supersalesmanship—there is one reported incident where potential airline customers physically barred their doors. As a result of these efforts, Lockheed lined up sufficient potential airline customers for their *commercial* version of the C5A+, the whale-shaped, 400-passenger, L-1011 airbus called the TriStar. Things looked really good.

Meanwhile, back at McDonnel-Douglas, they had developed the DC-10, an airbus that some airlines thought was superior to the TriStar. Indeed, in early 1968 American Airlines announced the purchase of twenty-five DC-10's at a price of some $400 million and the race (some called it carnage) between Lockheed and McDonnel-Douglas was on!

In their eagerness to sell the TriStar airbus, Lockheed shaved the price of the L-1011 to $1 million *below* the DC-10. As one Wall Street hand put it, McDonnel-Douglas has been "sandbagged."

Dan Haughton, Lockheed's president, adopted a peculiar strategy. By "buying in" to the Air Force C-5 contract in the hopes of subsequent commercial business, and then shaving the profit on that business too thin, he sowed the seeds for the ultimate disaster that resulted. However, Haughton apparently was so busy in his role as a salesman—a very effective one, incidentally—that he failed to develop proper plans and to subsequently establish controls for the inevitable overruns. These overruns began to occur within two months of the final contract signing in 1966. Instead of 115 planes, the Air Force decided to buy only 81.

The worst is yet to come

By January of 1970 the cost estimate to build 81 C5-A's had risen to $3.7 billion—against an original estimate of $1.4 billion. Things began to look bad for Lockheed. In May, 1970, Deputy Defense Secretary David Packard delivered secret congressional testimony and emphasized that a merger was the best solution for Lockheed. Without it, he said, there probably would be no alternative other than receivership. At this time, Lockheed was seeking $641 million from the Pentagon as claims on disputed defense projects.

In February of 1971, Lockheed reluctantly accepted an out-of-court $200 million loss settlement on the contract. It was thought that this settlement, plus additional financing that Haughton could arrange, might permit Lockheed to squeeze through on the defense contract and continue production of its commercial TriStar as well. Recall that the engine supplier for the TriStar was Rolls-Royce, Ltd. of England. The TriStar (L-1011) was to have the Rolls RB.211 engine that embodied the very latest technical developments anywhere in the world. Incidentally, Rolls was having minor technical problems with the RB.211.

Meanwhile, at Rolls-Royce—in order to monitor and control the joint program between the two companies, Lockheed and Rolls-Royce had established bi-monthly meetings between key personnel of the two firms. Once each month the meeting would take place in England and once in the Burbank headquarters of Lockheed. It was during the occasion of one of these routine meetings in London that Lord Cole, chairman of Rolls-Royce, Ltd., and Daniel Haughton, President of Lockheed, sat down for a luncheon of sherry and cold salmon on February 2, 1971. For months, Rolls-Royce had been concerned about the financial stability of its American partner. Lockheed has been concerned with technical delays at Rolls-Royce. Haughton looked forward to telling his host that Lockheed was about to nail down the additional financing that was required for the TriStar.

Lockheed has settled that matter with the Pentagon by accepting a $200 million loss on the C5A airforce transport. Second, and this is due largely to that settlement, the company just about nailed down the financing needed to continue full speed with Rolls-Royce and TriStar program.

The Rolls-Royce story is a sadder one. The outside auditors confirmed what was suspected for some time. While the company was able to clear up most of the technical difficulties with the Rb.211, the development was behind schedule and the engine was not performing as expected. Second, and more important, the costs had gotten completely out of control! The company suspected something six months before when the loss for the first half of 1970 was $115 million. Now the auditors calculated the estimated cost of bringing the RB.211 into production was $600 million. The 1968 estimate was $156 million. Finally, and worst of all, the British Government has refused to contribute any more to the $113 million they had already sunk into the program. Indeed, the Board asked the company's debenture holders to appoint a receiver. *The company was bankrupt!*

Incredible as it may sound, Haughton received the news of the failure of Rolls-Royce barely forty-eight hours before it was announced in the House of Commons and to the world press. Things couldn't have been blacker for Lockheed.

Temporary recovery

At the time of Rolls' collapse, almost $1.7 billion was committed to the project—$900 million by Lockheed, $350 million by subcontractors, and $400 million by Rolls and its subcontractors. Moreover, nine airline customers (Eastern, T.W.A., Delta, Air Canada, etc.) and twenty-four banks were deeply involved. The enormous complexity of getting these parties to act *in concert* was expressed by the then Secretary of the Treasury John Connally who advised Haughton: "Dan, your trouble is you're chasing one possum at a time up a tree. What you've got to do is get all those possums up the tree at the same time."

It was to the great credit of Haughton that he was able to bring order out of chaos and ultimately salvage the TriStar and Lockheed—temporarily. The salvage deal involved essentially the British Government's pledge to subsidize production of the RB.211 engine and Lockheed's agreement to increase the price they would pay for the engine. Haughton, in turn, had to re-negotiate with each airline customer and keep each of them from being the first to desert what looked like a sinking ship.

Survival for Lockheed depended upon Congressional approval of a $200 million loan guarantee. However, approval of the loan brought forth the most vociferous of Lockheed's critics. Senators Alan Cranston and Mike Mansfield wanted a clean sweep of top management. Ralph Nader suggested also that the top managers at Lockheed be fired for "mismanagement." Another member of Congress called Haughton and his top management "a merry band of thieves."

More problems

After the settlement that was engineered by Haughton, development on the TriStar and the RB.211 engine continued. However, problems with orders began. Second-buy orders were lost or failed to materialize. Some of the losses could probably be traced to another planning and design failure; the lack of a design that would permit the TriStar to be adaptable to an intercontinental version which the foreign airlines wanted. To rectify this design mistake and produce an intercontinental version required 60 percent new components and a more powerful engine that would raise the engine price another $200 million.

Clearly, Lockheed managers had not followed fundamentals in the inception and development of the C5A and TriStar (L-1011) problems. The effects of overlooking these fundamentals were cumulative. Bad news followed worse. The company adopted a strategy of trying for an emphasis on commercial business by placing their bet on the TriStar. However, as the company entered 1973, the orders for the plane were far below the break-even point. The plane's image wasn't helped by the tragic crash of an Eastern Airlines' TriStar with a loss of 100 lives in the Florida Everglades in January 1973.

The poor image of the company was reflected in the stock market where a total value of less than $100 million was placed on Lockheed (compared to $1 billion for McDonnel-Douglas).

Rolls-Royce: a legend passes

"To the British, the news of Rolls-Royce
was like hearing that Westminister Abbey
had become a brothel."
—Manchester Guardian

This legendary maker of the world's finest cars had been in the business of aircraft engine manufacturing since World War I. During the intervening years it had earned an uncompromising reputation for technical excellence and performance. During the decade of the sixties, Rolls-Royce, under the leadership of Sir Denning Pearson, became the seventeenth biggest company in Britain, with 87,000 employees and gross sales in 1968 of $720 million (80 percent in aircraft engines). Its engines are found in the planes of 180 airlines and 60 air forces.

Despite the reputation of Rolls-Royce and its relative success with certain engines, it could never develop the mass markets of American manufacturers *unless the company could break into the American market on a major scale.* Breaking into this market became the overriding consideration and the major component of company strategy. These considerations, plus an overriding concern with the technical excellence of the company, became the foundation for its ultimate downfall.

Joy turns to gloom

Sir Denning Pearson decided to implement his new strategy of "get into the U.S. airbus market at all costs" by sending his engineer/salesman, David Huddle, to New York on a quasi-permanent basis. Huddle went all out to sell the new RB.211 and was later knighted by the Queen for his efforts in landing the Lockheed contract.

When Lockheed decided to buy the RB.211 in April, 1968, Britain went ecstatic! In fact, *the terms of the contract were a disaster for Rolls-Royce!* What they committed themselves to do was deliver an engine that: (a) was *twice* as powerful as the next most powerful in airline use; (b) used a new, untested material incorporating a design principle untried in commercial jets; and

(c) was to be delivered in 1971 at a development cost of $156 million. In retrospect, this task was extraordinarily difficult if not impossible. In their eagerness to crack the U.S. market, the management of Rolls was seduced by their technical ability (of which they had a great deal) and in the process was unable to muster their managerial ability (of which they had very little).

Rolls-Royce did two things well. First, their sales work was superb. David Huddle took up residence in the U.S. to head the sales effort that paid off. They designed a better mousetrap and sold it. Huddle established the RB.211 early as the engineers' favorite over the competitive engines of GE and Pratt & Whitney. Second, they had earned a reputation as a company with design skills second to none. Engineers, airplane users, indeed almost everyone associated with jets agreed that the RB.211 was superior.

It is sad to think that the foregoing skills were not matched with managerial ability. During the autopsy that inexorably accompanied Rolls' failure, it was widely observed that their management was strong on technical ability, but "strangely silent when finance or management was mentioned."

Incredible accounting

The incredible failure to maintain a modicum of control over development costs can be traced to actions taken by Sir Denning Pearson. In 1961 he changed accounting methods so that future jet development costs could be paid back when engines had been delivered instead of being paid for as they occurred. This account- ing "gimmick" allowed Rolls to report profits earlier, but sowed the seeds of later disaster when development costs on the RB.211 got out of hand. The attitude became one of "let the cost rise, we will pay it back when production starts." Actual costs were viewed as paper costs.

Even more incredible is the failure of Rolls management to discover the extent of their trouble until shortly before bank- ruptcy. Two years elapsed after signing the contract before action was taken. Prompted by a $115 million loss in the first half of 1970, the Government replaced Sir Denning Pearson as chairman, and ordered an independent audit. Although this audit gave some indication of the real extent of Roll's difficulties (development costs soared to $600 million vs. $156 million under contract), the liabilities could not be calculated because of what one official called "a lack of accounting."

The lesson of Rolls-Royce

Not since the abortive Suez expedition of 1956 had there been an event equal to the Rolls-Royce disaster for causing self-examination on the part of British businessmen. There was hardly a businessman in Britain who didn't do a little soul searching about his own operation. The editor of Britain's *Investors Chronicle* remarked: "Every board room in the land has been asking: 'What's the lesson in this?' "

Aside from the usual failure to obey management fundamentals, it appears that the major lesson to draw from the Rolls experience is the need for balance in an organization, particularly one in technology or engineering. The natural inclination in these firms is for the technical man, the creative engineer, to rise to the top and surround himself with the same type of persons. It goes without saying that the maintenance of sales, production, and finance within planned control limits is more difficult under these circumstances.

Junior's problems at Douglas

> Douglas said, "This is the plane we're selling.
> If you want it, buy it." *So we didn't.*
> —Airline Executive

This quote indicates the overconfidence that once prevailed in the management climate of Douglas (since merged with Mc-Donnel). This kind of optimism was high in April 1966, when President Donald (Junior) Douglas published reports that the company was "in one of the most satisfactory phases of its history." Earnings were over $14 million (more than 1965) and the stock had hit a yearly high of 112. Six months later, *losses* for the year were put at $16 million and the stock *dropped* to 30–a paper loss of $359 million–and dividends were suspended!

How many of the company's problems could be attributed to

nepotism? For almost ten years "Junior," as he was universally known outside of his presence, operated as *de facto* boss under the paternalistic veto of his father, Donald Douglas, Sr. Among "Junior's" innovations was a reorganization which resulted in the firing or resignation of ten vice presidents, a bloodbath that was discussed in subdued voices up until the McDonnel takeover in 1967. Shortly before that time Douglas executives confessed that their problems could be traced to a serious breakdown in corporate communications and controls. Production and marketing were running on different tracks. Most of them were completely unprepared for the trouble that followed.

After a belated start in the jet business and after losing out to Boeing's 707 for a time, Douglas came on strong with the DC-8 and DC-9, the latter plane exactly right for the market at the right moment. Ironically, Douglas couldn't stand success. To meet the demand, the company expanded production facilities too hastily and and lost control of costs. There were also some expensive production delays. The result: Douglas lost about $600,000 on each DC-9 it delivered.

Perhaps the luckiest thing that ever happened to Douglas is that it ran third (after Lockheed and Boeing) in the bidding for C5 Air Force transport.

It should be noted that McDonnel has pulled off an excellent rescue job on Douglas since their merger into McDonnel-Douglas in 1967.

Boeing missed the bus: fortunately

Few events in aviation history excited the interest that surrounded the 1970 flight of the Boeing 747—the 362-passenger "jumbo jet." However, the gaffes were as big as the plane:

> *Roswell, New Mexico.* Despite an FAA rule against photographing an evacuation test, a magazine photographer persuaded a Roswell citizen to simulate an evacuation from the 747. The obliging resident jumped into the evacuation chute, yelled "whoopee," and broke his leg.
>
> *Kennedy Airport. Inaugural flight to London.* Because of a 1000 to 1 freakish angle in a gusty wind, one engine on the 747 was deprived of air and heated up. The passengers had to be bussed to dinner while awaiting another plane. The first bus hit a car. The

second bus was hit by a car. The third bus got stuck in a snowbank. The fourth bus got hopelessly lost. The driver left his bus in a "No Parking" area while phoning for directions. A policeman came along and gave the bus a ticket.

These amusing but embarrassing incidents are indicative of some of the troubles that have beset Boeing since the award of the multi-billion dollar SST contract in 1966. That event marked both the high point in Boeing's history and, ironically, the beginning of a new period of trouble that ended in its efforts to outdo the industry in the "airbus affair." During the stock market slide in 1970, the market placed a value on Boeing of a mere $584 million, approximately the value the market placed on Memorex, although Boeing is 56 times the size of Memorex.

Boeing's troubles can be traced to the management of three major programs: The SST, their belated efforts to get into the "airbus" race, and production difficulties with their stable of planes (707, 727, 737, 747).

The SST crisis was not extremely costly (as compared to Lockheed's C5A), but it was bad news for Boeing's reputation. The announcement that the program was delayed for a year resulted ultimately in its cancellation. The company was in the position of having sold a program that *Boeing* thought was needed but that *nobody* wanted: a strategic mistake.

After the company woke up to the fact that they had no plans for a plane to compete with Lockheed's TriStar "airbus," President Wilson undertook a sales mission to sell the airline companies on the idea of *waiting* for a Boeing airbus that might never be produced. *No thanks,* said the industry. Frustrated, Boeing made a belated attempt to put an airbus in the air by modifying its own 747—an effort that was called "that Erector-set airplane."

Finally, the company was plagued by production problems on its 707 and 727. Parts shortages became so acute that production lines had to be shut down, with extra costs of at least $100 million.

General Dynamics: A not so dynamic organization

Roger Lewis, the only man in the very thin New York headquarters staff (of General Dynamics) with any significant general

> management experience, had a great deal of
> difficulty keeping tabs on his far-flung com-
> pany. "I could see that right away when I
> first got to New York a year ago," says Dave
> Lewis (New President).
>
>   *—Forbes,* October 15, 1971

It was amazing that an abysmal lack of controls continued to exist in General Dynamics (GD) ten years after their $470 million debacle in commercial jets. This 1961 titanic loss in the Convair adventure was attributable purely to lack of controls. Apparently some companies learn little from experience.

In view of GD's continuing oversight in management fundamentals, one wonders how they can stay in business. They have been consistent and heavy losers in commerical jets, shipbuilding, and defense. The $470 million Convair loss (1961) was the largest in American history until that time. Their venture into shipbuilding cost an estimated $40 million in 1968 alone, and this is probably conservative in view of some of GD's suspect accounting methods.

Their shipbuilding venture is typical of planning and control failure. After paying $5 million for Bethlehem Steel's Quincy (Mass.) shipyard, Bethlehem's president said he would have been happy to pay GD $5 million to take the yard off his hands. In 1973, ten years and a $280 million loss later, the company looks forward to making a profit on an order for cryogenic gas tankers.

After winning the much publicized TFX (F-111) defense contract, GD proceeded to experience the usual cost and time overruns. From an original estimate of $5 million per plane, the cost rose to about $8 million. Fortunately for GD the contract was signed before the "fixed cost" edict of Secretary of Defense McNamara. Because the F-111 contract is "renegotiable," GD may not be hurt too badly. Can we speculate what would happen if they were bound by a "fixed price" contract such as Lockheed's C5A?

LESSONS TO BE LEARNED

Some major lessons to be learned from the experiences of companies in the aerospace and defense industries include these:

Maintain organizational balance. Don't let technical or engineering excellence (or excellence in any one area) blind you to the need for organization *synergism.* Marketing, operations, and finance are important too.

Don't "buy in" to a product, market, or deal. This is a desperation move. If you take the calculated risk of losing money—you usually do.

Don't get rich with a pencil. Visions of high sales and high profits that are forecast without adequate planning seldom come to pass. Be careful of seducing yourself.

Adopt a strategy of selected diversification . . . if you are a one product/service company. Don't put all your eggs in one basket (product, customer, market, etc.).

Plan progress and costs and maintain tight control over them. Events just don't happen. They must be *made* to happen. Accounting and other controls are essential to achieve a plan.

Chapter 3

PENN CENTRAL: THAT'S NO WAY TO RUN A RAILROAD

"Penn Central was a managerial bankruptcy before it was a financial one."

—John Barriger
President
Missouri-Kansas-Texas Railroad

The middle 1920's was the golden age of railroading. The Pennsylvania became known as "the Standard Railroad of the World." The New York Central, put together by Cornelius ("Commodore") Vanderbilt, enjoyed its finest years as it boasted of the country's most punctual freight and passenger service, led by a great fleet of Pullman trains racing from New York to Chicago over the "water level route." The stocks of both companies were considered as safe as Government bonds.

Although railroad operations and profits were in a secular decline during the next forty years (in the words of the great Jim Hill, " . . . passenger trains were like the male tit, neither useful nor ornamental.") the stock of the *combined* railroads was selling for as high as $86 per share in 1969 and the *stated* assets exceeded $6 billion.

In 1970, the Penn Central (the merged Pennsylvania and the New York Central) was bankrupt! The series of events leading to this bankruptcy provide one of the most incredible stories of mismanagement in the history of American industry. The man ge-ment of Penn Central not only violated most fundamentals of management—they invented some new ones.

Railroading: The problem of rational costs

Any ordinary manufacturer or service business that is confronted with a huge earnings decline can go to work on products, pricing, salesmanship, operations, or management. Obsolete or unattractive products can be upgraded or dropped. Inefficient operations can be cut down or reorganized. If existing prices are not selling the goods, prices are restructured.

By and large, these alternatives are not available to U.S. railroads. For over 85 years, the railroads have been regulated by the Interstate Commerce Commission, and for even longer they have been a favorite target for the extortions of special interests, tax collectors, and labor monopolists. Almost everywhere they turn, the railroads are hauled up by regulations, rulings, politics, court decisions, and so-called arbitration and mediation.

Shortly after the bankruptcy, Penn Central's president, Alfred Perlman, attributed this conglomeration of the rail industry's ills as the cause of the company's woes. Later the court-appointed trustees were to summarize these problems under the label of *rational costs,* the thesis that railroads should only be required to absorb costs that were *rational.* Consider the argument:

(a) only 60 percent of railroad track is profitable; the remainder should be abandoned;

(b) rate regulation should follow a variable costing principle, with below-cost rates outlawed;

(c) work rules should be changed to provide for rational manning requirements or government subsidy should be provided.

However, despite the protestations from Penn Central's management that the absorption of these non-rational costs was the real reason for the railroad's difficulty, the facts reveal quite a different story. Moreover, it is only fair to ask: "If Union Pacific, Southern and other railroads were able to remain profitable despite the same problems (and somewhat less profit potential), why couldn't Penn Central?" The answer lies in incredible *mismanagement!*

Pennsylvania-New York Central:
A marriage with no honeymoon

As Chairman of Philadelphia's huge Pennsylvania Railroad Company, Stuart Saunders used to count the days and the hours until he could consummate the long-planned merger between his company and the New York Central. Once the merger was complete, his troubles would be over—he thought. He would have one of the great opportunities in U.S. business: a synergistic combination of two great railroads.

In February, 1968, Saunder's wish came true when the two railroads merged. However, the taste quickly turned to ashes. His problems were bad enough before the merger. They were compounded and accelerated after the merger. And Saunders could not—or would not—provide the management needed to arrive at a viable, profitable operation. As the president of a competing road concluded: "The merger was not a failure. The two railroads were never merged. The marriage was never consummated; it was a civil war. Take the most prosperous railroads in the country, the Southern Pacific or the Union Pacific, run them the same way and they would go bankrupt." Apparently, Saunders had learned the hard way what the conglomerates were beginning to suspect—synergism is great in theory, but difficult in practice. Later, Saunders was to comment: "All this (operations, physical plant, personnel) has got to be molded together, and if you think you can make a marriage like that and have a honeymoon. . . !!"

The merger was doomed from the start because of organizational difficulties, conflicting personalities, and the sheer enormity of the combining task. This was particularly true in view of the unmoving convictions of the two former presidents, Stuart Saunders of the Pennsylvania (later chairman of the Penn Central) and Alfred Perlman of the New York Central (later president of the Penn Central). John Barriger, President of the Missouri-Kansas-Texas Railroad and an old hand in the business, concluded: "The Penn Central mess is caused by corporate schizophrenia. There were splits among Saunders and Perlman that got more personal as time went along. The organization was running off in three different directions at once. At the operating level, this polarized people into identifying themselves with the red or green team, never with Penn Central."

Perhaps a honeymoon was too much to expect from the merger of the two antagonists. Indeed, they had secretly admitted incompatibility before the "I merge with thee" vows were taken. Recriminations between Saunders and Perlman often became personal. Perlman felt that Saunders, a lawyer, was no railroad man; Saunders felt that Perlman was sabotaging merger negotiations. As chairman and president, respectively, of the merged company, the two were unable to bury the hatchet of ancient rivalries and provide a smooth meshing of the two railroad properties.

Safeguards that failed

The series of events leading to the downfall of the Penn Central are even more remarkable in view of the nature of the company's business and the safeguards that presumably protect the public from mismanagement. These include, first of all, the Interstate Commerce Commission (ICC), whose staff regulations and close supervision are designed to insure that railroads operate in the public good. Second, the usual audit by a public accounting firm should turn up evidence of any fraud, deception, or extraordinary mismanagement. Neither of these safeguards worked.

None other than Ralph Nader, the protector of American business conscience, accused the ICC of failing the public in the Penn Central case. Not only did this agency fail to foresee the onrushing debacle that led to bankruptcy, but it should never (according to Nader) have approved the merger in the first instance. The ICC, for its part, defended its role in approving the PRR-NY Central merger and maintained that the Penn Central suffered its financial plight as a result of "internal conflict and external pressures" that were not under ICC control. Inflation, obsolete labor practices, tight credit and a long and severe stock market decline were among the reasons given by the ICC for the failure of the railroad.

A great number of people blamed the firm's auditors, Peat Marwick, Mitchell & Company for not revealing the troubles that were surely evident long before the downfall. L. Spacek, a noted spokesman for the public accounting profession, blamed the profession for closing its eyes to the facts concerning the railroad's operation and asserted that the profession could have disclosed the Penn Central situation long before it broke down. He noted also that the profession had been aware of railroad accounting deficiencies for fourteen years.

The management of Peat Marwick, Mitchell & Company defended their accounting practices and audit procedure by asserting that no accounting firm can be responsible for the kind of management decisions made by the Penn Central.

Railroad or conglomerate: Penn Central's confusion about corporate purpose

Even before the PRR-NY Central merger, the "senior partner"–Pennsylvania Railroad–had experimented with diversification. Using cash that he had obtained from Norfolk and Western stock and from sale of the Long Island Railroad to New York State ($65 million), Saunders bought 90 percent of the Great Southwest Corporation and built the Six Flags Over Texas amusement park. This investment ultimately jumped in value from $60 million to $312 million, and the success went to Saunders' head. He rapidly acquired Macco Realty, Arvida Corporation, and Buckeye Pipe Line. Then, after the merger with the New York Central, he acquired or purchased other operations including hotels, coal fields, oil refineries, investment companies, and sports teams (e.g. N.Y. Knickerbockers, N.Y. Rangers). Real estate holdings in Manhattan alone exceeded $1.2 billion. After the 1970 bankruptcy, the trustees decided to sell off these properties in order to ease the overwhelming liquidity crisis. Two-hundred-thirteen potential bidders paid $100 each for documents describing individual properties. However, actual cash bidding was slow. The company is lucky to receive a fraction of book value—when it rains it pours.

This diversification "kick" made Alfred Perlman particularly virulent. He was convinced that whatever cash was available for diversification should have been spent on railroad improvement. Even before the merger, he would say, "I'm putting every cent I can find into making this (New York Central) a better railroad. I'm not putting it into some silly amusement park." (A dig at the Pennsylvania and Saunders.) As events subsequently proved, Perlman was right, and Saunders was wrong. A little more attention (and assignment of cash) to "running the railroad" and less attention to the misguided diversification gamble would surely have avoided the inevitable consequences of a strategy that turned sour.

During the autopsy that followed Penn Central's collapse, many self-appointed pathologists diagnosed their illness as *"diversification disease."* Among the healers who attended the wake was Congressman Wright Patman of the House Banking and Currency Committee, who had the power to raise the railroad from the dead with a government approved loan of $200 million (a loan that he ultimately granted). He claimed that the hangover from the acquisition binge was the real reason for Penn Central's problems. The hangover included a severe cash squeeze which in turn diverted management's attention from the true purpose of railroading.

Indirectly, the railroad's misguided gamble in diversification was to contribute to its ultimate downfall. When real estate values stopped their spiral in the late 1960's, the liquidity crisis tightened. One result was that Standard & Poor's bond rating service reduced Pennsylvania Company's rating from a triple B to Bb, a rating described as "borderline between a definitely sound obligation and one where the speculative element begins to predominate." Shortly thereafter, the company attempted to market $100 million worth of debentures, admitting in the prospectus that "there was no assurance that these values (real estate ventures) could be maintained in a liquidation." In view of this combination of events, the new financing failed and the *railroad filed in bankruptcy.*

The question remains today: If the same amount of cash and management attention had been directed to railroad operations, would not the railroad have avoided disaster? The answer must be in the affirmative.

The board of directors:
see no evil, hear no evil

During the three week period shortly before and immediately after Penn Central's announcement of bankruptcy, at least ten members of the board of directors resigned. Although the specific reasons for quitting were not always clear, it is easy to conclude that they did so because:

(a) there was no point in staying aboard a sinking ship (or railroad),
(b) there was some evidence of involvement in actions that were somewhat suspect, and
(c) stockholder and creditor suits were almost sure to follow.

At any rate, subsequent events and testimony reveal that the board discharged its duties in something less than acceptable fashion. Among its shortcomings were failures to adequately supervise railroad operations, capital acquisition and distribution, and basic corporate strategy.

Operations

It can be fairly assumed that the board either endorsed or went along with Saunders' policy of delaying and overlooking basic road and equipment maintenance in order to conserve cash for other purposes. In post-bankruptcy testimony, a trustee and former Secretary of Labor, Willard Wirtz, stated that "the corporate policy at the time was to put the best conceivable face on the facts to the point that these facts were dubious allies of the truth."

This policy of desperately trying to make the income account look better by inadequately maintaining track and rolling stock had the inevitable effect of diminishing the supply of serviceable freight cars. This in turn led to poor service, followed by reduced business, which in turn led to a severe cash flow problem and the dreadful circle was compounded.

The sad state of operations was well known in the industry. W. Graham Clayton, Jr., president of a much-better-run railroad (Southern), ran a hobby railroad of over forty feet of track in his backyard. In an obvious dig at Penn Central, he lamented: "It suffers from deferred maintenance."

Dividends and Cash Flow

According to the Interstate Commerce Commission Report, Penn Central and the predecessor companies (Pennsylvania R. R. and New York Central R. R.) paid out $292 million in dividends between 1963-69 while net income for the same period was a mere $2 million. Dividends were not suspended until 1970, the year in which the railroad's net loss was estimated to be $431 million.

Incredible? Yes!

It is hard to believe that responsible and informed directors would permit the continued payment of dividends while the company was experiencing a *negative cash flow*. This is simply carrying a policy of "putting the best face on operations" too far.

Diversification

It is now clear that Saunders and his management team (Perlman excepted) were intent on running a conglomerate—not a railroad. The excuse that return on investment was potentially greater outside the railroad industry was not sufficient reason to embark on an entirely different strategy. Yet the board of directors obviously concurred and permitted this change of direction.

Perhaps the most persuasive salesman for diversification was D.C. Bevan, the financial vice-president. In an incredible attempt to shift the blame for the results of this diversification policy, the Penn Central Transportation Company later blamed Bevan for counseling the railroad's directors to make substantial investments in non-railroad ventures. Bevan himself was later to be charged with unlawful conspiracy and other alleged acts in connection with private gain from this diversification program.

More typical bloopers

Consider the following amusing mismanaged events of the Penn Central.

Item: In Akron, there is a grain elevator where railroad cars are emptied by being lifted and tipped over, with the grain pouring into bins. One day a bunch of cars came in from Penn Central, and they were lifted and dumped— they were filled with bathtubs.

Item: Englewood Yard is a key assembly point for freight
          trains headed east from Chicago. Because any train
          longer than 79 cars would require an extra brakeman if
          the train crossed Indiana, Penn Central kept the trains
          down to 79 cars in order to save the wages of the
          brakeman. The result was a pile-up of cars outside the
          state, delayed shipments, and under-utilized loco-
          motives.
          Old hands said that freight yards are the bowels of a
          railroad, and that Penn Central was badly constipated.

Item: The annual meeting of Penn Central, originally sched-
          uled for May, had to be postponed "at least until June"
          because financial statements were not available.

Item: The company's unspoken policy of "delayed main-
          tenance" caused breakdown of cars and equipment.
          Shippers, fed up with decaying service and top level
          bickering, switched to trucks.

Item: In March, 1971, the case of the missing 227 Penn
          Central freight cars came before a Federal Grand Jury in
          Philadelphia. It was noted that the possibility of the cars
          having been scrapped was unlikely because this required
          a lot of work for a small return, and freight cars are
          almost impossible to fence.

Item: Alfred Perlman says that the heart of the merger pro-
          blem is the incompatibility of the two railroads' com-
          puter systems. Penn Central could no longer locate cars
          on its line; the daily rental charges it paid other roads for
          cars in use on its lines went through the roof; shipments
          that normally required six days to deliver took 18 to 22;
          and as shippers began routing their business to com-
          peting lines, the railroad's traffic volume ebbed.
          Perlman said: "All of a sudden they were in the dark and
          we were in the dark."

Item: In the final few months preceding bankruptcy, Saunders
          was voted a pay boost of over $42,000 by the board of
          directors.

Item: In House testimony one month after Penn Central's
          bankruptcy, Saunders called the railroad unmanageable.

Shenanigans from inside?

One of the remarkable sidelights of the Penn Central disaster
was the fact that few persons on the outside knew it was coming.

Wall Street was very slow to turn sour on the company. One unbelieving ex-broker (now a cab driver in New York) remarked shortly after the debacle: "I was putting my customers into Penn Central at sixty. Can you believe it? How is it possible? A company with $6 billion in assets. Six billion!"

The event that precipitated the crash in the company's securities and led directly to bankruptcy was the failure of a $100 million debenture offering. However, a careful observer could have forecast the onrushing failure by watching the actions of those officers and directors inside the firm. Insider selling accelerated significantly even before the debenture offer failed. At least fifteen executives began bailing out as *inside* information of the impending disaster became obvious. Naturally, these people denied to SEC that they had access to inside data. Saunders was quick to admit that he incurred heavy losses by retaining his shares— inferring that he either did not know about the impending failure of the company or that he had faith in the stock value.

The "insider" charge was repeated by Congressman Wright Patman as he called for a probe into the propriety of trading in the stock by nine institutions; over 1.8 million shares were disposed of by these institutions between April 1 and June 21, 1970. These sales included 590,000 by Allegheny Corporation and 436,300 by Chase Manhattan Bank. Patman asserted that many of these sales were undertaken with "greatest clairvoyance or on the basis of insider information." Quite naturally, this claim was categorically denied in the strongest of terms by the institutions involved.

The ultimate in alleged insider collusion came more than one year after the company's collapse, when D.C. Bevan was indicted for causing company funds to be diverted into his own investment company. He and several other persons associated with and active in Penn Central management were charged with organizing and manipulating an unlawful conspiracy that caused the railroad to suffer heavy losses by reason of its having invested in Penphil (Bevan's investment company) to the tune of a $66 million loss.

Post bankruptcy

Penn Central went bankrupt because of incredibly bad management, lack of governmental supports and stubborn and short-sighted union demands. Many doubted that the railroad could ever become a viable entity. Two and a half years after the trustees and the new management took over, Penn Central is in deep trouble. It can't even go into bankruptcy because it is there already. Since June 1970, Penn Central Transportation has lost $1.4 billion. 1972 loss was an estimated $225 million. 1973 is expected to be a little better—maybe only a $150 million deficit. The cash drain is bigger than ever. The working capital is down to five days operating needs.

Changes are needed: faster and more drastic. This is difficult under a judicial trustee management. The creditors may try to force a distribution of assets and the nationalization of the railroad. Another year should tell the story.

LESSONS TO BE LEARNED:
PENN CENTRAL'S MESSAGE FOR MANAGEMENT

Does the biggest bankruptcy in the history of American industry hold out any lessons? Can we learn from their experience? Consider these:

Don't underestimate the difficulties of merging two unlikes. Salad oil and vinegar won't mix unless shaken vigorously. The cost of running two merged operations can be greater than the combined cost of running them individually. Watch out for the "synergism" cliché and the "economies of scale" argument.

You can't combine two camps and keep two chiefs (e.g. Saunders and Perlman). One chief has either got to go, or accept the other as the boss.

Don't depend on the establishment to protect you. Government agencies, regulatory bodies, consultants, accountants, and other watchdogs have interests that may conflict with your own.

Get a strategy and stick with it. Determine what business you're in and mind the store. Don't go off in too many directions (diversifications.).

Demand participation by the board. A "rubber stamp" or "window dressing" board is about as bad as none at all.

Demand loyalty and clean skirts from insiders. When executives go into business for themselves they are likely to neglect their job with the company or develop a conflict of interest.

Don't sacrifice corporate longevity to a short term problem. Manipulating the books, panic cost cutting, delayed maintenance and other means of "putting on a good face" will eventually cost you two dollars for every one you save

Chapter 4

AIRLINES: PAN AM'S NOSE DIVE

Scene: Dulles International Airport, Washington, D.C.

Event: Christening of the long-awaited flight of the Boeing
747—the 362 passenger "jumbo jet."

Mrs. Richard Nixon christened the first 747 by pulling the
lever on a spray device that showered the plane with a fountain of
red, white and blue water for the benefit of millions of viewers on
color TV. An employee under the platform activated a pump
which sprayed the water. The lever that Mrs. Nixon pulled had no
other function other than to signal the employee under the
platform.

When the time came to turn off the water, nothing happened.
Mrs. Nixon pushed the lever several times and looked embarrassed. Najeeb Halaby, President of Pan American Airlines,
pushed it and nothing happened. The band played the National
Anthem and nothing happened—the water continued to flow.
Finally, Halaby hurried under the platform to find the pump man
gazing at the sky, lost in fascination at the beautiful rainbow he
had created.

This amusing but embarrassing incident seemed to typify a
series of events gone wrong for this once great American airline.
As the company prepared for the mid-seventies there was some
doubt that it could survive as a viable enterprise. "Emotionally I
just can't believe Pan Am could go under," said one high official.
"But rationally, I can see where it might."

What happened to this prestigious airline? It has long held a
special position in the mushrooming travel industry. Its inter-

national business is four times that of its closest U.S. rival, Trans World Airlines. Its premier, globe-circling route system takes it to the most glamorous cities of the world: London, Paris, Rome, Berlin, Tokyo, Johannesburg, even Moscow. It is by far the world's leading carrier of air freight, a big potential profit maker. Pan Am was the first airline to fly the 707 and the giant 747. It was the first airline to diversify into hotels. Yet, in the three-year period 1969-71, it managed to lose over $100 million. Despite the depressed nature of the airlines industry, this performance is substantially worse than any other major airline.

Not since 1961, when Howard Hughes was ordered to pay $136 million for mismanagement of TWA, has there been such a bad case of poorly run airline operations.

Pan Am's chairman, Najeeb E. Halaby, was very vocal when confronted with the question: "What's wrong with Pan Am?" He blamed the federal government—arguing that the company must be granted a domestic route network and that excessive overseas competition must be reduced. He also argued that Pan Am should be allowed to merge with another U.S. carrier (but he could not find a willing partner).

These contentions do have some justification. In common with all airlines, Pan Am has had to live with spiraling wages and fare reductions, but Pan Am had additional problems in its accelerating competition from scheduled airlines, and the proliferation of non-scheduled charter operations. However, if Halaby expected his salvation to come from Washington, the future of the airline remained seriously clouded. What was needed was improved *internal management,* something that there has been very little of in the past few years. Indeed, any college junior taking a management course would have little trouble spotting Pan Am's management problems. The company provides a textbook case of doing most of the right things the wrong way.

Organization: office-of-the-president syndrome

It would be an understatement to say that Pan Am's chairman, Najeeb Halaby, was an organizational anomaly. Few chief executives have cut such a wide swath (and with such a sharp axe) in organizational structure and personnel at all levels. Acutely conscious of the fact that he was regarded as an inexperienced interloper by many at the upper organizational levels, Halaby felt it necessary to consolidate his control by a purge of the organization. Between those who were fired outright and those who quit because they were offended by Halaby's egotism, three dozen upper-level managers departed during his first two years in command.

Halaby found himself in trouble when his executive vice-president chose early retirement. There was no one with direct, full-time operating responsibility. When an urgent search for a chief operating officer *outside* the firm failed to uncover a willing candidate, Halaby devised a most unusual and peculiar organizational structure. He decided to have four presidents instead of one.

With the advice of industrial psychologists he appointed four group vice-presidents and divided operational responsibilities among them. All four of these group vice-presidents (called "groupies" by insiders) were recent arrivals from *outside* the company, and were rather inexperienced in airline operations and therefore unacceptable to other managers in the organization. In fact, the four group vice-presidents and the men filling the positions became the butt of the company-wide jokes. They were variously called derisive names such as "The Alexandria Quartet" and the "Four Horsemen of the Apocalypse." Later they were known as the "Four-In-Tandem."

In a press release announcing the creation of the group vice presidents, Halaby said, "We want to have a smart, sensitive, flexible, quick-to-respond group at the top to meet the deep challenges that threaten the basic character of our industry, and to anticipate the rapid and dramatic changes that lie ahead." What he got was confusion, conflicting operations, slow decision making, and low morale.

Although Halaby said that one purpose of the reorganization was to reduce his span of control, the four-way division of responsibility created additional problems when the "groupies" could not agree. These disagreements were frequent because of the incongruities in duties. Functional, geographic, territorial, customer, and product organizational lines overlapped. One of the group vice-presidents who resigned because of the pressure said, "There is a tendency for walls to be erected, which is not desirable in a one-business company. Because there's a group, many things don't get done that should be done—a lot of things fall between the cracks. And it takes too many levels of management to make decisions."

Worst of all, Halaby made it clear that the four men comprising "The Alexandria Quartet" were competing for the presidency—a situation hardly conducive to the cooperation necessary to make such a system work.

Finally, in late 1971, Halaby's better judgment and the board's insistence forced him to select a president—a retired Air Force Brigadier General and former head of the Air Force Academy. William T. Seawell assumed the post of Chief Operating Officer, but, Halaby was still the CEO and in command.

Management depth

Among several managerial deficiencies existing at Pan Am, some could be traced to the legendary Juan Trippe, the company's founder, and a tough act to follow. It became clear that he did not anticipate the managerial needs of the company. Management development was almost totally ignored. Who needed planning and management when Juan Trippe was around? Such a philosophy eventually got them into trouble.

Upon his ascension to the chief executive's spot, Halaby compounded the trouble. Admitting that he was ill-prepared for the job ("I was vice-president miscellaneous"), he did little to alleviate the lack of talent when he went outside the industry for most replacements. Including himself, five of Pan Am's top six executives have relatively limited airline experience—or none at all.

The situation was not improved when some of the newcomers displayed ill-disguised scorn for the few veterans that were left after Halaby's purge. One long-haired, forty-year-old who was hired from Western Union did little to improve morale when he referred to pre-Halaby executives as the "faded aristocracy."

In 1970 alone, Pan Am announced the appointment of over thirty—yes, thirty—vice-presidents. That was the year they lost $48 million, worst in history.

Planning: management by crisis

Juan Trippe, Pan Am's founder, was a pioneer in aviation and a giant in the airline industry. However, he was not one for new-fangled management ideas, and consequently did not feel the need for formal planning; there was no group or organizational entity assigned that functioned during his reign.

Although Halaby appointed a senior vice-president for planning, his duties were largely long-range in nature and did not extend to operations, where money was made and lost. Moreover, there is evidence that no one adequately foresaw, or prepared for, the combination of events that soured the company's profitability Halaby himself bragged about being "Mr. Outside" and saw his role as the company's ambassador to Washington, rather than as an operating executive who planned and controlled day-to-day operations. He was public relations conscious, and even in his days as administrator of FAA (he was Kennedy's second choice) he rushed around the country making personal appearances that brought him a great deal of public attention, but stirred up a lot of controversy about how well he could administer.

Given this climate at the top, and the organizational hodge-podge of four group vice-presidents running the "president's office," there is little wonder that plans were not achieved if, indeed, they were ever developed.

When seat factors (the percentage of seats occupied by paying passengers) dropped in the face of rising passenger loads by competitors, a series of sales meetings were held on a "crash" basis in a desperate move to sell more tickets. Little attention was given to discovering and curing the *why* of falling sales. Frantic moves were made to cut costs by reducing the number of available seats in line with declining traffic. This meant reduction in the number of flights, which in turn reduced their market share still further.

In a typical managerial style of panic, the company reacted to falling revenues and profits *after* the situation became critical. Budgets were slashed, thousands of employees were laid off—cost reduction became the password. At all levels in the company unhappiness was widespread, as the future of the company and individual jobs were endangered. One manager said scornfully, "Everybody was writing SYA memos—save your ass." The committee management in the president's office could yield no decisions. No one was really in power, and yet they were all trying to be in power.

Two camps

Much like Penn Central with its two opposing camps (the Pennsylvania group and the New York Central group) Pan American had its "newcomers" and "old-timers." The "old-timers" by-and-large were holdovers from the Juan Trippe era, and most of them outdated Halaby. Many of these vice-presidents and executives were former pilots, and a number of them returned to their jobs as senior pilot (sometimes with a pay increase) rather than face the uncertainties present in the managerial ranks. Those who remained were either hanging on until retirement or they became bitter at the carnage wrought by Halaby in what most believe to be his indiscriminate wielding of a new broom.

The platoons of "newcomers," particularly those at the top levels, were largely inexperienced in the airline business. They believed in the "transferability of skills" theory that says a manager in one type of business can be a manager in any type. Most were "mobile managers" with experience in several industries—but not airlines.

The relations between the two camps can most generously be described as an uneasy truce. However, one disastrous result was low morale and disgruntled employees at all levels—and, if there is one thing that disgruntled employees can do effectively, it is to *drive away customers.* Can the plane fly with a divided crew?

An airline on the couch

While serving as administrator of the Federal Aviation Agency, Halaby became convinced that recent findings of psychology could be used to improve interpersonal relations in a business environment. Since morale was sagging at Pan Am because of poor interpersonal relations, he hired a psychologist, Dr. Robert Snowden, brought him into the councils of top management, and gave him extraordinary latitude to improve interpersonal relations throughout the company. Snowden's advice was sought on the abilities and personalities of top executives. He was consulted on such other diverse matters as which type of organizational structure would be most effective. In a most unusual action, Halaby even suggested that Snowden would talk to executives who were having trouble communicating with Halaby.

Company psychologists got on the "sensitivity" bandwagon in the late 1960's and set up a sensitivity training program in Montauk Point, from which not even the highest ranking executives were exempt. The programs became a company joke. Even worse, executives and employees began to resent them. A stewardess laughed: "We get $60 in overtime for attending, so why should we care?" Although lower level employees tended to treat the program as silly and inconsequential, those at top management levels bristled with frustration. One thirty-five-year-old vice-president who took his 100-man staff to a session recalled: "After a couple of days, the psychologists gave up in frustration. They said we were the most hopeless group they had seen, and that we might as well go home."

The presence of the psychologists in the company, and particularly at top levels, became a joke. The carnage caused by Halaby could not be improved by ramming better interpersonal relations down the throats of those affected, nor could sensitivity training restore profits that were eroding through poor strategy and operational management emanating from the "groupies" in the office of the president.

Morale on the rocks

Morale—motivation—is beyond a doubt *the* most important ingredient in any organization. Indeed, it makes the character of the company, and without it there is only a matter of time until mediocrity or failure sets in.

This is doubly true in the airline business. The *only* thing that distinguishes one airline from another is the service personnel—the people who come in contact with the public. It is these people—and little else—who give one airline a competitive edge over another. A courteous, attentive, interested, motivated service

employee—pilot, stewardess, ground crewman, ticketing or termi
nal employee, counterman—can make or break an airline. There
isn't an executive in the industry who will deny this fact.

Despite this obvious need, morale in Pan Am was allowed to
deteriorate almost to the vanishing point. This was true in the
lower ranks as well as near the top. Why was this so? Consider the
following:

> *Merger.* It was common knowledge that Pan Am had for years
> been searching for a viable senior partner with whom they could
> merge. This search was undoubtedly given impetus in the late
> sixties when Pan Am almost became the victim of the con-
> glomerate acquisition binge. Gulf & Western and a crap-shooting
> company called Resorts International (formerly a small paint
> company named Mary Carter) almost took control.
>
> Later it was Halaby's announced strategy to engineer a merger
> with another airline. His choice for courtship was T.W.A. How-
> ever, this competitor dropped the marriage proposal in late 1971
> when it became obvious that Pan Am's operating figures were, to
> say the least, unattractive. T.W.A.'s question was: "Why should
> we take on a sick partner?"
>
> After a turndown of his proposal by T.W.A., Halaby
> proposed marriage to Eastern. But it is also evident that any
> merger proposal will have to wait until Pan Am's own manage-
> ment has improved its performance enough to make reasonable
> terms possible.
>
> What has been the effect of Pan Am's preoccupation with a
> merger strategy? First, it has diverted Halaby's attention from the
> real problem of Pan Am—operations—to an external attempt to
> get others to salvage the company. More importantly, it has
> significantly reduced the motivation of Pan Am management and
> employees. Who wants to work for an outfit whose days are
> numbered?
>
> *Organization:* Despite the fact that several board members were
> demanding that Halaby name an operating executive—a presi-
> dent—he elevated four men without experience either in Pan Am
> or in the airline industry to "the office of the president" in an
> attempt to share these responsibilities. This action destroyed
> morale at the top. This, of course, inevitably flowed downward to
> all levels of the company.
>
> *Style of Leadership:* Whether it came from his former bureau-
> cratic experience or from his belief in the questionable conclusions

of the behavioral scientists, Halaby chose a misguided style of "participative" leadership on the one hand, and "absentee" leadership on the other. He paid lip service to participative management, as evidenced by his weekly recorded telephone pep talks to employees. However, some of these talks were something less than motivational. Listen to one that was made in a week of particularly bad news:

> "The fact is that we've gotten off to a bad start. We're trailing behind last year's pace—a year in which we sustained the highest loss in Pan Am's history. Not only is our net loss for the year larger than programmed, but our share of key markets is down. We're feeling the recession now as we did not feel it in the summer of 1970 and we're hurting."

Negative attempts such as this to "motivate" employees, plus his consistent absence and detachment from operating problems, combined to produce a style of leadership that was hardly a positive influence.

What's the next step?

In April of 1972, Halaby was forced to resign and Seawell assumed the positions of Chairman of the Board, President, Chief Executive Officer and Chief Operating Officer. He was given free hand to rebuild the airline. But he has a hard and a long task before him. It only takes a short time for a company to plunge down from the pinnacle of corporate success to near bankruptcy; it takes years to effect a turnaround. In four years—1969 through 1972—Pan Am managed to lose some $150 million dollars. Will Seawell be able to reverse the trend? Will Pan Am ever reach again its undisputed leadership position of the middle sixties? It's too early to tell.

Eastern Air Lines: A lesson about customer service

Until 1960 Eastern had been the most consistent moneymaker in a precarious and highly volatile industry. In the early postwar years they continued to pile up earnings while the industry was going through a drastic shakeout.

These profitable years could be attributed largely to "Captain Eddie" Rickenbacker, the strong-willed chairman. Because of him, and *in spite of him,* Eastern prospered *in the short run.* His frugality and cost-consciousness became industry legends. He even extended this philosophy to passenger service. He could get away with it in his near-monopoly routes between New York and Miami.

Eastern's ticket sellers and gate attendants became renowned for a brusque officiousness hardly calculated to win friends; the unspoken attitude was that the customer was lucky to be allowed to fly with Eastern. Things got so bad that an informal organization called WHEALS—We Hate Eastern Air Lines—came into existence. Customers were completely alienated. The attitudes filtered down to Eastern employees and resulted in slowdowns and poor morale.

Eventually, around 1960, Eastern's poor customer service image caught up with them and they spent the next decade trying to rid themselves of this image. Meanwhile, profits plummeted. Finally, after ten years of trying, President Floyd Hall has succeeded in reversing this image at great cost to the company.

The message here is one that all chief executives in service industries should note. So often, the customer's entire impression concerning the company is a function of how well they are treated by the service employees. And, if these lower rank and file people are not sufficiently motivated, the future of the company is at stake.

LESSONS TO BE LEARNED:
SUGGESTIONS FOR A SERVICE INDUSTRY EXECUTIVE

Based upon the correlation between Pan Am's sorry operating record and the violation of management principles by its chief executive, certain lessons can be learned by the executive in any service industry:

Authority and responsibility cannot be shared by a group. The classical principles of scalar chain and unity of command are still pretty good.

Don't pay lip service to participative management. If you want to practice participative management (a good idea), don't fake it—subordinates can spot it, and you.

Be careful of the "Behaviorial Scientists." The laboratory research findings of the psychologists have immense potential for the executive, but these findings must be implemented with great care.

Maintain some management depth. If you *must* go outside for managers, consider hiring them yourself rather than asking a consultant or "body snatcher."

Avoid management by crisis. Proper foresight and planning can frequently avoid the problem before it arises.

Avoid splitting people into two camps. People, and groups of people, working against themselves can destroy an organization.

Avoid, at all costs, low morale by employees who meet the public. In a service industry, the only thing that distinguishes you from the competition is the behavior of your service personnel—those who meet and deal with the customer. A disgruntled or discourteous employee can turn away hundreds of customers.

Chapter 5

COMPUTERS: SNOW WHITE AND THE SEVEN DWARFS (RCA, GE, Univac, Control Data, NCR, Burroughs, Xerox)

> "Do you know we actually had two guys whose job it was to keep us out of the computer business? It probably saved us half a billion dollars. The worst thing we could have done is gone down that road."
> —Harold Geneen
> Chairman, IT&T

How many directors, chairmen, and other top executives have wished that they had adopted the philosophy of this incredible manager, Harold Geneen? Consider the corporate giants that have tried to edge into the mainstream of computer manufacturing, only to back off or fail miserably. RCA, General Electric, Westinghouse, Hughes Aircraft, Bendix, Ratheon, General Foods and Philco-Ford are among these. Is it, as a top computer executive admitted, "because companies failed to realize that computers were a business and not a technological romance?" Or is it because, once again, we see corporate giants overlooking management basics? Perhaps it is both.

Something indeed did go wrong, as we can see from examining fact and fiction:

FICTION	FACT
"Except for a minority of skeptics, computer men believe their business is entering an era in which all but the incompetent or the inordinately unlucky are destined to fare handsomely." —*Fortune,* August 1968	As of 1972, the rate of shipment of computers has not improved since 1968. Hundreds of software firms dropping out.
"We intend to be the Ford of the computer business." Bill Norris, Chairman Control Data Corp. (1967)	In 1971, return on equity was 2.9% and company ranked *sixth* in the industry.
"We aim to achieve a strong second place." Van Aken, General Mgr. Computer Dept., GE (1964)	Called it quits in 1970. Merged into Honeywell-GE and got 18.5% on a temporary basis before phasing out.
"We expect to be second only to IBM and we expect to be profitable." Robert Sarnoff President, RCA (1968, 1969)	Called it quits in computers in 1971. Loss $490 million.

Except for IBM and Control Data, the major firms in the computer industry are multi-product, and computers represent only one operation of several. If this were not true, many of them would have been unable to survive the fumbles, the management errors, and the strategic blunders involved.

The computer industry is like no other. It is not the technical hardware of the nature of the product that concerns the major computer makers but a matter of *survival strategy.* In an industry so big and with so many participants, it might seem that the companies would have a wide range of strategies available to them. In fact, their *only available strategy is to react to IBM!* The manner in which the individual firms have reacted is largely the subject of this chapter.

You might ask, why study IBM? The answer lies in the nature of the industry. IBM is the "fortress" and all assaults upon it have failed. The history of business in the United States contains many examples of companies who succeeded by a ferocious determination to make headway against what seemed to be insuperable competition. But no industry has thrown up a company so formidably powerful in everything that counts as IBM—and things aren't going to get better!

So if we can discover what makes IBM tick, and its *competition* fail, some valuable lessons will have emerged; perhaps some lessons for those inside as well as outside the industry. We note particularly that despite the track record of some of the big giants (GE, RCA, Univac), a number of smaller firms (Texas Instruments, Fairchild Camera, etc.) have plans for cracking the nut. Our advice: read the story of Snow White (IBM) and the Seven Dwarfs (RCA, GE, Univac, Control Data, NCR, Burroughs, Xerox).

Fortress IBM

> "If I found it necessary to raise some money, I would liquidate a painting or a jewel rather than sell a share of my IBM."
> —Stockholder comment (to loud applause)
> Stockholder Meeting—April 26, 1971

Perhaps this stockholder's loyalty is overstated. Or is it? Three months later, Tom J. Watson, Jr., 57, announced that he was relinquishing the offices of chairman and chief executive of IBM. This move marked the end of a great tradition of Watsonian leadership that guided IBM from a tiny, disorganized tabulating-equipment manufacturer to its present position among the very top industrial corporations of the world. And incidentally, if you had joined Tom Watson, Sr. in 1914, when he founded the Computer-Tabulating-Recording Company and bought 100 shares for $2,750, your investment would have risen to over $25 million.

In 1960, hardly a decade had passed since the installation of the first business computer. Yet IBM had moved into a position of competitive strength unparalleled in business history. They had over 70 percent of the market, a position they have yet to relinquish. Moreover, this market share gives them 90 percent of the profits.

It is a case history in outstanding management to examine those policies that put this company where it is. These policies can then be compared to the failures in order to see why they failed.

Service

IBM has a widespread advertising slogan today: *"We sell solutions, not just computers."* This philosophy is not new; it has been with the company since inception, and perhaps more than any other policy has accounted for the success of the company. Purchasers of computers know that support services (programming, software) are more important than the machine. Moreover, they know that they can get these services from IBM when needed. The "We sell solutions" approach results in a "multiplier" effect on sales. The real selling begins after delivery of the machine. Maintaining the world's largest stock of software, programmers, and educational facilities, IBM invites customer personnel, from top management to machine technicians, to spend some time at one of their several training facilities. After this, the salesman and systems engineer show the customer how the computer can solve more and more problems. The chances are good that, with proper follow up, the customer will discover sufficient new applications that will cause him to buy *additional* capacity. This process continues until the customer is "locked in" to the combination of IBM hardware and service.

Selling

If there is one corporate philosophy that has pervaded IBM from the beginning, it is the notion that the company is a sales organization—a philosophy that has given the company their prominent position despite the fact that they were never regarded as a pacesetter in the technology of computer hardware. No computer manufacturer has had much fear of the technical aspects of IBM because all manufacturers could design just as good or perhaps better machines. However, they couldn't match IBM in *selling* the machine.

From the beginning, Tom Watson, Sr. adopted the policy that a salesman who lost an order without exhausting all the resources the company had to offer deserved to be drawn and quartered. This company way of life was a serious one and was reflected in the organizational maxim that few men could rise to line executive positions unless they had spent some time selling.

In summary, IBM's marketing strategy was simple but effective, and could be expressed in the two-part approach: "We sell solutions and not computers," and "after the sale, hold the customer's hand." This strategy confused and confounded the competition because it had built a fortress that others were unable to assault. This frustration was expressed by one competitor in the mid-sixties after IBM had produced their now famous System/360 series: "And now IBM is selling real computers—alas!"

Lease vs. buy

Aside from their marketing strategy, the next most important reason for IBM's relentless hold on the industry is financial—and this in turn is due to their long-time policy of leasing rather than selling their machines. The idea is to keep title to most, if not all, of your output by leasing for a monthly fee. The advantage is that you can depreciate this investment on an accelerated four-to-six year basis, thus making the investment disappear from the books much faster than the machines disappear in the field. The result is a huge bank of hidden assets in the form of fully written-off equipment that does not appear on the balance sheet, but is still earning revenues.

In the industry, this bank of leased equipment is known as a "rental deck" and has been the major stumbling block (next to marketing strategy) for other manufacturers. Not even RCA or GE could afford the fantastic sums necessary to "carry" such an investment until it began to pay off. IBM, on the other hand, has a "rental deck" in excess of $20 billion despite the fact that it is carried on the books at only $3 billion. This deck is known in the industry as "IBM's bank" and it is a *money machine* unique in the history of U.S. industry. In one recent year, the company drew $5.5 billion of its $7.5 billion in revenues from this "money machine." As one frustrated competitor quips, "What makes IBM such a fortress is cash, resources, cash, liquid assets, earnings, and cash."

Organization

In these days of the real blunders—Convair, Edsel, Lockheed's C5A, and RCA's computers—it is to the credit of IBM's tight organization that their biggest product blunder was a mere $20 million mistake called STRETCH, a giant computer in 1960-61 that didn't sell or perform to expectations. To the credit of the organization, the company and Tom Watson learned a lot: "Our greatest mistake in STRETCH is that we walked up to the plate and pointed at the left-field stands. When we swung, it was not a homer, but a hard line drive to the outfield. We're going to be a good deal more careful about what we promise in the future."

IBM has always maintained and deserved an image of a chillingly efficient organization, one in which plans were developed logically and executed with crisp efficiency. Despite this image of efficiency, the company has not been impersonal. Indeed, it is hard to find a company in which the employees are so totally dedicated to the organization. In the case of its salesmen, the dedication borders on idealization. To quote a dated metaphor of a successful former sales executive, "Going to work for IBM is like joining the New York Yankees."

Much of this credit goes to Tom Watson, Sr., a businessman who linked his moral beliefs to management principles. When Tom Watson, Jr. took over from his father in 1956, the evangelical atmosphere and missionary zeal remained, but was overlaid with a new dedication to the disciplines of science. These various facets of the company (reflected in the motto—THINK) combine to provide an organization that facilitates the practice of good management principles.

Product

IBM's approach to, and success in, their product lines reflects the efficient organization described above. Their products have been developed very carefully, but have not been particularly

spectacular. It must be recalled that with over 70 percent of the
market, they are competing largely with themselves in introducing
radical product departures. It is somewhat like the quandry faced
by the auto industry when they introduced the mini-car, a product
that competed directly with the Maverick, Mustang, Camaro, and
Duster.

The company's decision to produce the System/360 series of
computers was the biggest commercial project in business history.
At about $5 billion, it was even greater than the SST (later
abandoned).

The decision to produce the System/360 has emerged as the
most crucial and portentous, as well as the riskiest judgment of
recent times. It has been called IBM's $5 billion gamble, or "bet
your company," in view of the likelihood of corporate failure if
the gamble didn't pay off. Fortunately it did, and this is a credit
to the company's organization and good management.

The success of this product decision made the next one easy;
the introduction of the System/370 series in 1971. This "fourth
generation" of computer hardware is destined to further solidify
IBM's hold on the industry—a hold that is not so much the result
of superior products, but the strategy of "selling the hell" out of
these products.

RCA: Number one in electronics
(But never in computers)

> "If you want to go into the computer
> business, ask David Sarnoff. He had all
> the right reasons to go into it."
> —Anonymous RCA competitor
> 1971

If anyone should have gone into the computer business it was
RCA. In 1957, under pressure to protect its reputation in industrial electronics and tempted by the potential of the multi-billion-
dollar computer market, RCA took the plunge. On and on they
plunged, from 1957 through 1971, through rivers of red ink,
recurring rumors that they were dropping out of the business,
countless staff reorganizations, a failing reputation in electronics,

and finally a disaster in 1971. When the final score is added up, the product write-off for RCA—somewhere between $400-500 million—could exceed any other single loss in history.

What went wrong? Did RCA fail in the fundamentals of management that IBM was so successful at?

Strategy

Shortly before disaster hit in 1971, the top management of RCA was paying lip service to a strategy that included computers as the main thrust of the company. For public consumption it was announced that their most serious efforts were going into computers and electronic data processing (EDP) and that they expected to be second only to IBM. However, there was never a *commitment* to this strategy. The computer division was looked upon as just another profit center of many other profit centers, and for years there was an uneasy but unsaid feeling that the eventual demise of the division was a matter of time.

The *specific strategy* for the computer division was ill-conceived and too long overdue for change. This strategy was simply to *mimic IBM!* It was amusing in the industry and probably worked to RCA's disadvantage. They bore the brunt of such industry jokes as this one: "RCA computer manuals are just as good as IBM's— they even have the same spelling errors."

This "head on" strategy fired its last broadside in 1970 when L.E. Donegan, General Manager of the division (and an ex-IBM supersalesman) came up with his strategy of "interception." This approach attempted, by underpricing IBM, to persuade existing users of IBM equipment to make a changeover to RCA's equipment. The idea was to offer them an alternative to the additional cost of moving up to the then newly introduced line of IBM System/370 machines. The strategy, as one Honeywell executive said, "Doesn't seem credible in the long run." *It wasn't!*

Selling and service

It was never a secret at the level of RCA's top management that marketing and service operations were far behind those of IBM. They probably also recognized the need to improve these operations. Whether from lack of control at the top (RCA's executive vice-presidents ran their divisions as independent dukedoms) or lack of commitment to strategy, the changes came too late and with too little detailed consideration.

In 1969, when Robert Sarnoff took over as chairman from "the General," he determined to close the gap between RCA's marketing and its recognized technological ability. Unfortunately, before this strategy was "geared up" with a sufficiently trained field force, the disaster had struck. Comparing RCA's sales force to that of IBM was like comparing the Boy Scouts to the U.S. Marines.

Pricing

In implementing their strategy of "going head on with IBM," RCA designed (in copy-cat style, it was said) a series of computers aimed directly at Series/360 users. RCA's had more capacity, was priced lower than IBM's new series, and RCA offered the potential user a very attractive price on changeover. This tactic failed because: (a) RCA didn't have the trained sales force and systems engineers to deliver the goods, and (b) IBM's loyal customers were "locked in" to IBM because of past good results.

Organization

It is doubtful whether RCA ever made the organizational commitment to become successful in computers. They assumed that they could pirate from and mimic IBM. This approach got them off to the wrong start when RCA hired a management consultant whose close relationship with IBM was presumably on a confidential basis. Thereafter, IBM management resolved to "kill RCA."

The organization of RCA could best be described as "loose." Vice-presidents of divisions "just dropped in" to see General Sarnoff to talk over problems, and this "let's talk it over" approach to problem solving was widespread in this $3 billion company. Ironically, when an operations staff was organized, among their first recommendations was one to get out of the computer business. This leads to the speculation that a good organization would have prevented the costly entry into the business in the first instance.

Control

A number of things indicate that the operations of the computer division were out of control. The news that RCA was abandoning computers came after close of business on a Friday afternoon, immediately following a board meeting where the decision was made. Second, the decision to quit computers came just a few months after the appointment of Julius Kippelman as fiscal officer of the Computer Systems Division. "He went out to the field and found out what the real story was, and it was a lot worse than corporate knew." To say that there was confusion in RCA is to underestimate the lack of control over operations. It appears once again that the multiproduct conglomerate type of organization that prevailed at RCA inhibited the type of control system that would have forewarned of impending disaster in time to take alternative measures.

General Electric

In March 1970, the "gunslinger" Wall Street analyst Martin Simpson remarked, "GE is sick, sick, sick. It's an overextended behemoth. They lost the strongest man they had in the computer area in an airplane crash." Later in September of that year, GE effectively called it quits in the computer business by merging with Honeywell and forming Honeywell-GE, an operation that gave GE an 18.5 percent interest. This merger is also destined for mediocrity if we believe one computer software executive, who snapped, "It's putting a sick heart in a cancerous body."

Of all those major companies that entered computer manufacturing, only RCA was in a better position to profit than General Electric. They got off to a late start in 1959 after landing a $30 million job from the Bank of America. At that time it looked like they had everything going for them. Despite the fact that GE has long been regarded as one of the best managed corporations in the world, they bit the dust in computer manufacturing with a loss measured in the hundreds of millions. What happened?

GE's downfall came as a result of managerial factors essentially the same as those at RCA. First, they figured they would make a killing in computers. Before they woke up to the fact of what it took to compete with IBM, it was too late. Although GE, like RCA, had the technical excellence and the hardware, every bit as good as IBM's, they did not have the sales and service organization to support it. Neither did they have the corporate dedication or commitment to these two important factors.

Second, GE, like RCA, was a varied and multiproduct company and was not organized to give computers the attention they deserved. Fred Borch, GE's Chairman, reflected this fact in his post mortem comment: "The major thing we've learned (from computer fiasco) is that the minute we identify one of these ventures as one of the few honest-to-God opportunities around, I would hope my successor would put the top guy he can find in charge of it, irrespective of its size at the time. It may be a little $20 million peanut. But, if that peanut could be $500 million one day, then the top man ought to pretend it is $500 million right now, and give it the $500 million kind of organization, of talent."

Managers and potential managers should take note of Borch's comment about organization. In GE's case it led not only to the computer debacle, but to perhaps even greater mistakes in the areas of nuclear power plants and jet aircraft engines, big losses for GE. Only an $8 billion giant could survive managerial blunders of such magnitude.

Sperry Rand-Univac

> "For the first twenty years of the electronic computer's hectic history, Univac racked up an unenviable record of snatching defeat from the jaws of almost certain victory."
> —*Business Week*

Although Sperry Rand has not gone out of the computer business and has no plans to do so, its Univac Division (as in RCA and GE) has lost almost enough money to sink the parent. This is remarkable in view of the fantastic head start Univac had on the industry. By 1952 they had fully two-thirds of the computer brains and design talent in the United States, and by 1955 had developed and sold three of the now-famous Univac I's to the government. They could have emerged as the giant of the industry if good management fundamentals had been followed.

The near downfall and subsequent distant second-place finish of Univac can be attributed to confusion caused by managerial shortcomings—confusion about organization, management and marketing.

Univac's organization has never been clear from the time in its early life when its irreplaceable group of scientist and design talent split up over internecine warfare (one of the group, William Norris, quit and started Control Data Corporation, of which Norris is still president). The organization structure itself was weak, unclear, and without lines of authority.

Confusion in the management of the firm as well as in the group of top managers has also been evident. In 1964, *Fortune* remarked that few enterprises have had such incredibly bad management. Controls were non-existent, planning was done on a day-to-day basis; profit planning and control were largely overlooked. It was said that top management came up from the ranks of carbon paper and Cardex and that they didn't understand computers and were consequently afraid of them.

Marketing could never approach that existing at IBM. This selling climate is reflected by the remark of a recent design chief, who remembered the days in the early fifties when the Univac I was manufactured, and three of them sold to the government: "then we sat there and wondered if anybody would ever buy another one." As late as 1958, the forecast of the market potential for the Univac: a total of twenty machines could be sold!

In conclusion, we find in the case of Univac an organization and top management that treated the computer somewhat in the nature of a stepchild, and did not organize for it. After all, the computer was just one of many products. In the post-1965 period much of this changed at Univac. A new chairman began to establish plans and set performance standards in order to achieve them. A market strategy has been developed which puts hardware and design experience to use in large complex operations such as airline management, areas in which the future of time sharing and other complex and profitable operations lie. Moreover, the long-needed emphasis on marketing and services is developing. Univac may be on the road to recovery.

Control Data Corporation (CDC)

Like most companies, CDC has its good and bad points. However, CDC knew the computer business well and has been in perhaps the best position to profit from it. Their failure to achieve their potential can be traced to the usual oversight in management fundamentals.

Founded in 1957 by William Norris, its current Chairman and a man who learned about computers as vice-president of Univac, CDC raised revenues from practically nothing in 1958 to over $570 million in 1969.

Unlike the rest of the industry, Norris avoided the strategy of "going head-on with IBM." Instead, he adopted the strategy of "hitting IBM where they are weakest," in large-scale computers, time sharing, and big installations where IBM's equipment could not do the job. The rifle approach to the market was based on its ability to produce the biggest, most powerful, most sophisticated computer in existence. Except for some acquisitions in related fields (including Commercial Credit Corporation to finance their "rental deck" of computers), CDC stayed pretty much in the computer industry. Norris believed that the relative failure of the big multimarket companies (RCA, GE, Univac, etc.) was due to their lack of attention to their computer products. He was fond of saying, "To run a computer company, it is necessary to have top executives who understand computers."

His product and market strategy, plus his insistence on strict standards of costing and pricing, made CDC a profitable company in its early life. However, their computer expertise notwithstanding, the management of the company fumbled the ball because they did not understand or practice the basics of good management. Aside from the autocratic, one-man rule of Norris (one vice-president said, "People learn what he wants to hear and then they play it back to him"), CDC's failure to achieve their potential can be traced to *planning and control:*

(a) The assumption that the sophisticated users of their equipment would be able to design and produce their own software and spare CDC this expense. This turned out to be a false premise.
(b) "Running scared" and price-cutting their magnificent 6600 computer based on a mere announcement of a new line (360 series) by IBM, *despite* the fact that IBM didn't deliver for three years.
(c) A complete bust in their market forecast. The forecast in 1970 was that business would keep on booming, and as a result inventory was doubled to exceed $300 million. When sales went down, profits were drastically cut not only due to falling sales, but by reason of increased financing costs.

LESSONS TO BE LEARNED

The computer industry is like no other. It has one big winner (IBM), one potential winner (CDC) and a number of others trying to cut their losses or carve out a small niche. From the short history of this industry we can draw some valuable principles of management for the future:

Don't go to war with a popgun. If you go head-to-head with the proven leader, be prepared to bring up your heavy artillery.

Make a commitment to a chosen product or market. Whether or not you are a conglomerate or a multiproduct company, if you decide to assign substantial resources to new projects/products/markets—make the necessary corporate commitment to see it through. Either get in or stay out of the business.

Don't get seduced by the prospects of a sexy new product, particularly if it is in a high technology area or if it is capital intensive. Look before leaping.

Avoid a "copy-cat" strategy. Develop your own corporate personality, image, strategy, and policies. If you want to "mimic" the leader, be sure you can deliver the goods.

Organize for a commitment. If you're going to be in a market for long-run profitability, commit the necessary personnel and other resources and organize to get the job done. Some computer manufacturers either treated the product as a sideline or never really believed they were in the market to stay.

Chapter 6

CONGLOMERATES: SYNERGISM
AT LTV MAKES 2 + 2 = 3

"We got the mushroom treatment. Right
after the acquisition, we were kept in the
dark. Then they covered us with manure and
cultivated us. After that they let us stew
awhile. And finally they canned us."
—Former executive of company
acquired by a conglomerate

In the decade of the 1960's a new managerial concept was
born—SYNERGISM—the notion that the sum of the parts is
greater than the whole—2 + 2 = 5—the output of the total organization can be enhanced if the component parts can be integrated.
This concept was the rationale for the conglomerate form of
organization and in some ways was responsible for the conglomerate trend in American industry, a trend that has had greater
impact than any other in the twentieth century.

Although the basic idea was sound, most of the conglomerates
have failed because they overlooked management fundamentals.

Ling-Temco-Vought (LTV): Its rise and fall

Of all the conglomerates, Ling-Temco-Vought (LTV) and its
head, James J. (Jim) Ling, probably best typify the movement and
all that was wrong with it. He came on in a burst of glory during
the middle sixties with headlines such as these:

Jim Ling Achieves Fantastic Leverage. (1966)
Look at Jimmy Ling's Wonderful Growth Machine. (1967)
Jim Ling is the Darling of Wall Street. (1968)
LTV Moves from Nowhere to 38th on List of 500 Largest Industrials. (1969)

Jimmy Ling, the wonder boy of the merger movement and the go-go conglomerator of the sixties, was described by *Fortune* as "part prestidigitator, part brooding genius, and part wunderkind." This description was entirely appropriate for the man during his early rise to fame. He parlayed $3000 invested in 1946 in an electrician's shop into an enterprise that in 1970 ranked 14th (right ahead of DuPont) in sales ($3.75 billion). His acquisitions included many of America's largest, oldest, and most prestigious firms. Among these were Greatamerica, First Western Bank & Trust, Chance-Vought Aircraft, Jones & Laughlin Steel, National Car Rental, Wilson & Company, and Braniff Airways. Quite an impressive feat for a boy who dropped out of school at age 14.

Like several of the conglomerates whose meteoric rise to fame and paper fortune later became a falling star, LTV depended less on sound operational management of legitimate growth than they did upon a variety of accounting and financial manipulations. The growing house of cards unjustifiably raised LTV's stock price, which in turn cleared the way for further acquisitions, which in turn raised LTV's stock prices . . . and so on . . . and so on.

The rise

The major part of Ling's strategy—one that ultimately back-fired—was his now famous Project Redeployment, a plan that one Wall Street observer described quite seriously as "proof you can get something for nothing." Here's how it worked:

(a) Spin off operating divisions into separate corporations.
(b) Offer shares in these separate corporations in exchange for shares in the parent LTV.
(c) Retain the bulk of separate corporation's stock in parent.
(d) Create market value for parent's holdings in subsidiaries.
(e) Use "inflated" value of parent holdings (for example, book value of $18 million in one subsidiary had a market value of $117 million) to get a "lot of something for nothing." The lot of something for nothing usually included acquired companies with low multiples.

Ling bragged: "I once heard a man brag about not having any long term debt. That isn't a realistic situation or attitude. On balance, it's always better to go to the money market."

The fall

Mr. Ling evidently stretched his own advice a bit too far. Indeed, in the late sixties the bloom was off the rose and the worm had turned. LTV went to the money market once too often and found itself with a debt of $700 million—but what's worse, there was little prospect that earnings could even pay the interest on this staggering sum.

Despite the fact that in 1970 LTV ranked 14th among America's 500 largest industrials in *sales,* it ranked *499th in net income ($69 million loss)* and *1st in ratio of debts to assets!!!* Things became so bad that they were forced to try to peddle Braniff Airways, the only subsidiary with any real profit potential.

Although there were spectacular failures before LTV's fall (Merritt-Chapman & Scott, Penn-Texas, Automatic Sprinkler), this conglomerate reflected much of what was bad in the movement. One of Ling's favorite expressions was that "business is a war game." It appears that he may have won a few games (acquisitions)—and some battles—*but lost the war!* By 1971 the headlines attested to his failure:

> LTV Debt Is $700 Million—Can't Cover Interest
> Is LTV a Corporate Power? Or Is It a Wall Street Soap Opera?
> Jim Ling Meets a Fate Worse Than Bankruptcy—Creditors Run
>   the Show.
> Ling Ousted!

Honeymoon over in conglomerates

In 1969, Nicholas Salgo, the Hungarian-born ex-realtor who started Bangor Punta (another troubled conglomerate) with a potato railroad and an expropriated Cuban sugar company, predicted that in ten years there would be only 200 major industrial companies in the U.S., *all conglomerates.*

Apparently this go-go harbinger of economic shifts failed to account for the eminent demise of the conglomerate movement.

Growing tired of "arithmetic mergers" and "mergers by numbers" that had little substance, both the public and Wall Street became disenchanted. The once-highly-touted conglomerates became as dead as doornails. In the opinion of *Forbes.* "They may not have put all their eggs in one basket, but eggs, after all, are eggs—and sometimes they smash!"

Age of the un-merger

Meanwhile, back at LTV, things were "coming apart at the seams," and as a result the creditors and stockholders began to put severe pressure on management. In general, similar pressure was being exerted elsewhere as the movement faltered and began to reverse as a result of the reaction. The scene resembled a bunch of kids trading bubble gum baseball cards; the conglomerates began to trade their acquisitions back and forth. Just as the 1960's was the age of the merger, the 1970's became the age of divestiture. Headlines began to appear in the financial press:

Conglomerate Chain Letter Runs Out
The Move to Deglomerating
Time for Divestiture

Even prestigious *Fortune* began to have doubts: "Audacious acquirers are swallowing up corporate assets galore. But how will it look when the chain letter runs out?" By 1970 the great con-glomerate movement was generating widespread doubt, some apprehension, and no little dismay. Even some of the former architects of conglomeration began to have second thoughts. William Duke, who put together Whittaker Corporation and who avidly propounded the theory of *synergism* in the early days, suddenly came up with an idea—PLURALISM—a theory that an acquired company might fare better on its own than as part of a conglomerate. *How Nice! How Novel! How Elementary—and true!*

Obey commandments of management

It seems that in the early seventies the era of the conglomerates had come to an end—certainly those that had been built on financial razzmatazz. Some people said that they were a disaster area. Others went to the extent of labeling them morally reprehensible.

One development has been the accountants who revised their pooling-of-interests method of merger accounting. There is also the Justice Department, which insists that any large-scale merger proposals receive their prior approval. But the most promising development concerns the conglomerate managers who now shun the label "money manager" or "asset manager." They now have awakened to the fact that they must be operational managers who must return to the traditional fundamentals of management that involve making a product and selling it at a profit.

What does it all prove? That a company, no matter how cleverly capitalized, can be no stronger than its underlying business. All the bookkeeping in the world is no substitute for the solid jangle of a real cash flow and the real comfort of knowing that the business is well managed.

Using LTV as an example, let's briefly review that company's *Crisis in Management* and how they arrived at their sorry state by overlooking fundamentals.

Strategy

Ling's two favorite expressions were: "You can't use twenty-twenty hindsight" and "Business is a war game."

These expressions have come back to haunt him, because our twenty-twenty hindsight now tells us that he lost both the *game* and the *war* for lack of a *strategy*—or to say it another way, the *wrong* strategy!

William Miller of Textron, a much more successful conglomerate, concluded that the philosophy and strategy of such high fliers as LTV was: *"business fundamentals be damned,* jazz up the stock and on to the races!" This attitude led to literally hundreds of unlikely combinations in the acquisition binge of the sixties. Among these were the steel, airline, meat packing, sporting goods, and car rental companies acquired by LTV, which was fundamentally in the electronics and aerospace business.

While there is no objection to growth through diversification, the strategic blunder of LTV was to adopt "growth at any price and in any direction" as a philosophy of life. This strategy—or lack of strategy—naturally led to violation of most of the other fundamentals of management.

Control

TRW's Dave Wright, who is head of a very successful business (and just incidentally a conglomerate), commented on control: "We never did subscribe to the idea of buying a company and then turning it loose. We delegated authority, but we always had close control."

Contrast this philosophy of control with that of such companies as LTV and Litton, who ran their "portfolio" of companies much in the same way that a mutual fund runs their portfolio of stocks—buying and selling for the performance of the individual entity alone. Simply stated, LTV's companies were acquired to maintain the growth and stock price of the parent, with little attention being paid to the subsequent control of operational performance of the acquired company. The result—LTV grew so fast that things simply got "out of control," with no standards and measurement of operational performance.

Board of directors

When questioned about the contribution of his board, Ling said, with tongue in cheek, *"We've never had a negative vote."* This autocratic, strong-willed chief executive would broach no interference from anyone—board or otherwise. And the board had no objection to this method of operation—until disaster threatened. Too late, they turned him out.

Could not an active, participative, responsible board have averted disaster?

Organization

Ling was identified early in his career as a non-conformist "egghead." He deplored the classical organization structure and the programmed trappings that inhibited his individual freedom of action. Although he modestly admitted to some ability to "motivate people," the organization structure he built at LTV was devoted to a furtherance of his growth strategy with little regard to the operation of his "mergers" and "un-mergers." By and large, he put things together so fast that no chain of command and little organization emerged. The philosophy at LTV became: "Who's in charge here?"

Accounting

Ling himself attributes much of the trouble with conglomerates to "Mickey Mouse" bookkeeping by the "little shiny-pants accountants." Yet, despite his payment of lip service to this type of accounting, he constantly engaged in it in his diligent pursual of his strategy that he called "The Game: The Game of Building."

While there is nothing fundamentally wrong with LTV's "re-deployment of assets" strategy (it was used by Studebaker, Textron, U.S. Industries and others who had to get out of the one-product cyclical industry), he used it as a means to finance the growth game—and he paid for it in "funny money" that was generated by accounting manipulation.

The good guy—IT&T

Although LTV and several other conglomerates (A-T-O, Litton, Avco, Ogden, SCM, W.R. Grace, GAF, Bangor Punta, etc.) were being mismanaged and falling upon hard times in terms of growth and profitability, things couldn't be better among the well-managed companies such as TRW and IT&T. Compare, for example, IT&T's action in fundamentals:

Strategy	Growth through synergistic acquisition of companies that can achieve growth *internally*. International growth.
Controls	Assimilation of acquisitions into balanced corporate diversification with common financial planning and control, performance standards, and reporting.
Board	Demands performing, participative, competent board and works hell out of them.

One-Man Rule	Harold Geneen is an extraordinarily strong and capable leader whose philosophy is "I delegate but don't abdicate." He assigns fantastic responsibility to subordinates.
Reaction to Change	Doesn't only react but causes change. Noted for reaction to and anticipation of ecology and other social demands.
Accounting	Earnings improvement for 43 consecutive quarters. This blue chip conglomerate has made all of its acquisitions (which have been friendly) with equity securities instead of debt. Policy is full and accurate disclosure.
Organization	Planned to accommodate people and other organizations.
Management Depth	Geneen has such ability to develop talent that IT&T is known as "Geneen U." At least twelve IT&T executives have become presidents of other companies.

Postscript

James J. (Jim) Ling, controversial and colorful head of LTV, was deposed as chairman, president, and chief executive in July 1970. However, shortly thereafter he acquired Omega-Alpha and announced that his strategy would be to buy firms and split them. His old style of management will remain intact. At the beginning of 1973, Omega-Alpha had not yet turned a profit. Forbes called Ling the Harold Stassen of conglomerates.

SOME PEOPLE NEVER LEARN!!!

After Ling's ouster, the company adopted an operational strategy that returned to the fundamentals of selling a product or service at a profit. Although 1973 found the management still trying to unscramble the financial puzzle, *operations* had brought the company very near the break-even point.

LESSONS TO BE LEARNED

More than perhaps any other type of organization, the conglomerate (multicompany, agglomerate) method of operating and the results that they have achieved convince us that management fundamentals are indeed important. Those companies (e.g., IT&T) that have followed these fundamentals have achieved success. Those (e.g., LTV, A-T-O) who have not are now in varying degrees of trouble. From their performance over the recent past, we can draw some generalizations:

Be extremely careful of the synergism argument. Overwhelmingly, acquisitions have been pure investment decisions rather than attempts to achieve economies of scale. Theoretically, the benefits of size and agglomeration derive from integrating functions and reducing costs—economies of scale. But that's the very opposite of what conglomerates do. So don't try to fool yourself (or the public) that your justification for an acquisition is *"synergism."*

Financial statements don't necessarily represent ($) dollars. Good will, obsolete inventory, bad accounts receivable, and premeditated accounting manipulation are among those pitfalls to look for in making out your own or evaluating the financial statements of an acquisition.

The acquisition chain letter can't go on forever. Geometric growth through acquisition gets increasingly difficult. If this were not so, a handful of conglomerates would own the entire country.

Avoid the "jazz up the stock" syndrome. The stock that sells for an extremely high multiple based solely on growth through acquisition is inevitably headed for a downfall.

Avoid accounting manipulations. This device will eventually come home to roost when used to make earnings or other results appear to be what they are not.

Chapter 7

AUTOS: IS THERE A CHRYSLER IN BIG THREE'S FUTURE?

In early 1970 *The Wall Street Journal* headlined: "Chrysler faces liquidity crisis. Entire market jolted." A decade of ups and downs had come to a close for this troubled auto maker.

Along with Penn Central's bankruptcy Chrysler's falling fortunes had a great impact on the big bear market that culminated in 1970. Chrysler's own stock price took a slide from 72 to 16 as their more than $800 million debt began to worry banks and the public alike.

Continuing crisis: ups and downs

A decade earlier, in 1960, headlines were similar and indicative of an era of chaos and demoralization. Newberg, hired to correct past errors in production and styling and to stabilize an excessive financial drain, was fired after only nine weeks because of flagrant conflicts of interest. The company was heavily budgeted and had excessive overhead staffs.

Between 1960 and 1963, the new president, Lynn Townsend, moved fast and with great energy. New men were brought in, demoralized dealerships were revitalized, and conservative styling was modernized in tune with the times.

Townsend trimmed down administrative fat—some 7,000 white collar workers were fired. Plants had to be realigned, similar operations were consolidated and a strategic expansion was started to achieve a balanced line of models instead of just one "hot" car. Above all, Townsend instituted tight controls, established precise checkpoints and saved some $50 million annually by efficiency improvements.

Era of plenty with Townsend

Between 1963 and 1968 Chrysler bounced back in its character-istic yo-yo fashion. Its fundamental problem was that of being a *marginal* producer. Operations were so close to the break-even point that there was literally no "margin for error." The new management was determined to rectify that situation. Manu-facturing, distribution and sales became closely controlled. An immensely detailed daily flow of information was pouring into headquarters and was being carefully analyzed. Townsend was a highly successful "needler with figures." A new computer system was put into effect to schedule and control production. This was essential because of a more complicated mix of models and options, and yet the need for greater flexibility of production and faster deliveries. A new advertising and styling policy was adopted to appeal to the younger buyers and extend the market. The results were spectacular. Chrysler's market share rose from a disastrous low of 8.6 percent in 1962 to a high of 18.1 percent in 1968. Earnings that year were over $6, and the stock reached $72, a long climb from $8 per share.

The bubble bursts

More spectacular than the recovery was the downhill ride—Failure! Sales, earnings and stock plummeted once again to new lows. Why? How? What errors could have been committed by Lynn Townsend and his team, the same men that saved the company some six years ago and managed it beautifully since?

The answer again is simple: They violated the Ten Command-ments of Management and had to pay for it.

Management fundamentals missed

Once again, we see that Chrysler's *crisis in management* is directly attributable to fundamentals. Some of these are examined below.

Strategy

Three basic decisions on *strategy* contributed to failure.

Small car. Decision not to produce a small car in U.S. is proving costly. This is the repetition of the 1964 mistake when Ford brought up the super-successful Mustang. Chrysler's answer months later was the "no contest" Barracuda. Also the lack of prestige car at the opposite end of the market deprived Chrysler of the two "hot" selling segments.

Foreign Market. A late entry in the overseas market, Chrysler had to settle for "leftovers" and invested over $500 million o catch up. Some $200 million was poured into a Spanish venture which suffered from poor sales, poor quality, and overcapitalization.

Diversification. Lack of diversification plans and actions leaves Chrysler with all its eggs in one basket. Depending almost entirely (95 percent) on car sales, Chrysler remains vulnerable to the slightest downturn due to either overall economic conditions or its own styling errors.

Controls

Townsend—the ex-accountant with a computer brain—believed in tight controls, instituted them at Chrysler and turned the company around. But then he relaxed; became too cocky. He began to trust his "feel" and intuition rather than facts. And the downhill slide started all over again. Just a year of casualness was enough to change a $290 million profit into a $7 million loss. This reversal was caused by a sales decline of 6 percent between 1968 and 1970, showing that Chrysler had returned to being a *marginal* producer. Results also demonstrated the high risk of such a position. It is interesting to observe that Ford had a bad year in 1967 when its profits plummeted from $621 million the year before to $84.1 million. This decline of 86 percent was due to a drop of 14 percent in sales. But a profit position was maintained and the next year (1968) Ford increased its sales 34 percent and was back at the above-$600 million net income level.

Tight cost and overall controls are among the most important managerial tools. A moment of inattention to this fundamental can erase years of work and progress.

Board of directors

Boards usually move too slowly. Some are uninformed like the Penn Central, some are dominated like LTV was, some are just conservative and don't react to change fast enough. The Chrysler board always had "lively" times. It did move on Colbert in the fifties, it fired Newberg under pressure, and, best of all, it "discovered" Lynn Townsend, the saviour of the company in the sixties. But it then went overboard in its admiration of Townsend. It gave him free hand, considered him infallible and his team "the greatest ever." This was gross abdication of the duties of the board of directors: the trusteeship for the owners—the stockholders of the corporation. This trusteeship function cannot and should not be delegated to the chief executive officer under any circumstances.

The fast-changing pace of our external environment contributes to the shortening of the "executive success" period. Unless the "boy wonder" changes his policies or *modus operandi,* the spectacular coup of a year ago may be a disastrous flop today if the same "proven" methods are used again. As the chief executive officer has only *one* boss, the Board, the directors must watch his programs and actions to discharge *their* duties. After the profits skidded, Chrysler's board began to function again and made Chairman Townsend replace President Boyd, an ex-dealer, with a more aggressive, financially trained 46-year old Riccardo. A return to *CONTROL!*

One-man rule

Although Chrysler has historically been dominated by the man at the top, this style of leadership did not fit Townsend initially. But then the success changed his attitude. His feeling of power, adulation from the board, and the praise from business experts made him rely more and more on his own judgment. He began to surround himself with weak yes men like Boyd, whom Townsend named president after moving to the chairmanship of the board. But Townsend remained the real boss, retaining chief executive title and prerogatives.

Management depth

As our society and the business environment become more complex, the need for capable men at all levels of management becomes a matter of survival. However, management depth cannot be achieved by just hiring talent and paying them well. In order to keep talented managers, one needs proper treatment of personnel to maintain enthusiasm and morale. Also, it is always better to develop bench strength rather than pirate someone else's.

Chrysler, before Townsend, went through several reorganizations, changing from centralization to decentralization and back. Managerial philosophy was confused, and the result was demoralization and loss of capable personnel. Townsend began to shift men around, brought in some new blood and began to develop "all-around" generalists, experienced in *several* phases of the automobile business. Results began to show, but the essential long term continuity of such a program broke down after the initial start. Chrysler always had difficulty in keeping talent. On several occasions, GM offered to give the ailing giant some of its own top executives. The move was not altruistic; the failure of the junior member of the Big Three would increase the share of the market of GM to a dangerous high and provoke a potential anti-trust action by the Justice Department.

But Chrysler's working atmosphere was always too cold and impersonal. The company never was able to inspire loyalty or enthusiasm among its talented employees. Reorganizations, lay-offs, budget cuts and the uncertainty of the future were then—and are now—a way of life at Chrysler.

Reaction to change

Chrysler moves are after-the-fact. The management allows an unnecessary and costly build-up of staff and auxiliary manpower, and then fires them by the thousands to cut budgets. It builds in one month 135,000 cars against sales of 56,000—then cuts down production drastically, causing confusion and high expense. It misses the foreign market and pours out $500 million to catch up—still without much success. Because of lateness it bought "leftovers." It misread the customer mood and then was late in correcting the situation. Over-expansion in the face of a dete-rioting economy and lagging sales created a liquidity crisis. The five-year warranty pioneered by Chrysler cost more than $50 million a year and was rescinded far too late after the realization that it was an expensive mistake.

Even the deterioration of Chrysler's traditional high quality and engineering excellence was not counteracted vigorously in time, but allowed to skid, affecting image, customer confidence, and ultimately sales.

Customer's new power

The automobile industry is entirely dependent upon the cus-tomer. The belief that the customer can be influenced by the manufacturer is a costly if not disastrous concept. All the advertising, publicity, gimmicks and pressure from Detroit did *not* persuade the American public that cars should be bigger and flashier. The trend to small cars was the customers' idea and Detroit is tardily learning how to deal with the power of the buyer. The fashion industry had a similar experience when the women rejected the Paris designers' midi and liberated themselves (partly with "hot pants") from an imposed yearly fashion strangle-hold.

Chrysler missed the boat (or was it the car?) time and time again. While Ford was hitting the target of customer demand with the Thunderbird (luxury personal car with a sporty flair), the Mustang (for the young and the young at heart), and finally with the small economy car succession—Falcon, Maverick, Pinto—Chrysler was sticking to its big car concept. Because big cars bring bigger profits, Chrysler restyled its big car line at great expense in 1969. But the customer wasn't buying. Result—the Chrysler line sales declined 62 percent in two years. Despite this record, the company resisted the obvious: build a small car. The decision to import the Japanese-built Colt and the English-built Cricket was not an innovative strategy but a desperation move because of no plans to build a small car in the U.S. And yet, over 56 percent of new cars delivered in 1970 were in the small or compact category.

Computers

Computers are very, very good when they work and very, very bad when they don't. Chrysler used computer systems from the inception of the electronic era and pioneered many applications, particularly in inventory control and production scheduling. In the middle sixties, the company initiated an accelerated program of automation and mechanization, necessitating an extensive and complex computer system to schedule and control production. As the mix of models and options increased, so did the programming difficulties by several orders of magnitude. A key error was made at that time. The computer system was excellent for existing situations but had no built-in provisions for growth-expansion in volume, new cars, and shift in manufacturing facilities. In a word, it lacked flexibility.

When new production systems were instituted, lines were switched and plants were modified, and the entire computer system suffered a major case of indigestion. It became overtaxed. Make-shift remedies added to the troubles. Scheduling suffered and physical delivery of cars was actually delayed. Thousands of cars were built to wrong specifications and thousands of cars were shipped to wrong destinations. The dealer morale and confidence, lifted after years of doldrums, was again shattered. In the midst of lagging sales, Chrysler could not deliver the cars that were ordered. Misuse of the computer must share a lot of the blame.

Accounting manipulation

There is always a temptation to hide bad news from the public, from Wall Street, and from the banks. Chrysler's poor results in 1969 and 1970 resulted in the loss of a "prime" rating on their commercial paper. Because of this and their severe liquidity problem, any additional credit difficulties and bad publicity would have had dire consequences.

The tendency is to try to show higher profits and a better financial picture to retain credit lines. There is a slight indication that such maneuvers are not totally unknown to Chrysler executives. For example, in February 1971 the company changed its inventory accounting from 60 percent LIFO and 40 percent FIFO to all FIFO. The effect was to reduce the 1970 operating loss (on paper) while increasing inventory value, and hence working capital. The cost of this accounting change will be additional taxes of $53 million to be paid over twenty years!

Organization

Creative plans, innovative ideas, and modern policies will not help a company much if there is an inadequate organization to implement these changes.

Chrysler suffered through the years from extreme swings in its organizational structure—from centralization to decentralization and back. Emphasis shifted between engineering, manufacturing and marketing. Financial largesse for rapid expansion contrasted to drastic budget cuts and layoffs when expectations were not met.

The same Townsend who decentralized operations, created new divisions, and established a multiplicity of profit centers had to tighten the belt and recentralize operations for cost savings through closer control. Sales activities were pulled together into three units, as against seven separate marketing operations before. The faltering overseas operations have been consolidated into a semi-multinational company for better coordination. Ford did the same four years sooner.

The rigid production system is being changed into a more flexible one to allow faster changes in actual production between models, styles and makes.

Plants are being modified to allow building of different cars at the same location. The engineering and quality control departments are being revamped to regain the quality image.

Chrysler is reorganizing because the previous system did not work. The key factor appears to have been the lack of communications between staff and line organizations.

The classic line and staff principle did not work at Chrysler. The line neither respected staff nor did it follow directives or recommendations of staff people. On the other hand, *line* was removed from the market place and did not understand the changing customer moods.

Every company should basically follow a structure fitted to its "personality" and operating policies. Chrysler has not yet found the proper fit.

The good guy—Ford

Contrasting Chrysler's performance with that of Ford, we can see that Ford has been much more consistent and profitable. Can this be attributed to their better management? We think so! Let the evidence speak for itself:

Strategy	Expanded foreign market and went multinational. Forecasted shift in demand to small car and came out first with Pinto. Always moves fast to anticipate demand and meet it.
Board	Ford gets failing grade on use of board. Ford dynasty, represented by Henry II, remains unchallenged.
One-Man Rule	Although one-man syndrome in effect, Henry II surrounds himself with good team and listens to them.
Management Depth	Company is noted for depth and calibre of its management, starting with "whiz kids" of fifties. Keeps abreast and flexible, moving from

	research, technology, marketing as times demand. Ford makes it fun to work; Chrysler makes it a chore.
Reaction to Change	After Edsel debacle, learned to react fast. Entire company geared to sensitive changes in economy or market place. Management makes fast good decisions before "paralysis through analysis" sets in.
Customer	Realized changing mood of public; car no longer status symbol but just a necessary item of transportation. Complete antithesis of just a few years ago. All this means a lot to researchers and engineers and decision makers at Ford. Not so at Chrysler.
Computers	Ford computer system, while less elaborate and ambitious, was flexible enough to allow timely changes and the transitions into various models and switching of plants. Operations never hampered by computer errors.
Accounting	Never any need for manipulations because financial operations so much better than Chrysler. Percentage of operating income to sales is almost double Chrysler and long-term debt about half.
Organization	Ford's organization structure, and to a lesser extent its management philosophy, was patterned after GM many years ago under Breech. It has served the company well, and Ford has had necessary flexibility where changes were required.

Measuring management performance

A few figures speak louder than many words. The following table tells it as it is. No comments are necessary.

	General Motors	Ford	Chrysler
	in percent		
5 year return on equity	16.7	12.6	6.2
5 year return on total capital .	15.7	11.1	5.4

	General Motors	Ford	Chrysler
Latest 12 months return on equity (1972)	19.3	15.2	7.5
Latest 12 months return on total capital (1972)	17.8	12.8	6.2
5 year annual sales growth . . .	6.6	9.3	7.3
5 year annual earnings per share growth	3.4	14.8	(−7.4)

LESSONS TO BE LEARNED

(1) Controls pay off. Any company, large or small, must have tight financial and operational controls. The by-word of management must be controls, controls, controls.
(2) Delegation does not mean abdication. Performance of delegated responsibilities must be tightly controlled.
(3) Attention to details is not nitpicking but an essential and vital part of successful management.
(4) Strategic decisions are difficult and often painful—but they must be made. Delays are often more costly than a decisive early step (e.g. failure to introduce a small car).
(5) Board of Directors must be active and responsive."Rubber stamping" and blind belief in the infallibility of the chief executive officer are costly and unfair to stockholders.
(6) Management depth is not an empty "OK" term. It is a must for any company, and particularly for those enjoying or suffering from a "one-man rule." The increasing complexity of our technological world requires specialists and talented individualists—not men carefully selected for their ability to agree with the boss.
(7) Change is accelerating and so must the company's reaction to changing times—technologies—customer demands. The outside environment pressures must take precedence over the internal company environment and "evolutionary" policies.
(8) Organizational policies and structure must also follow the times. The key issue today is to provide better and faster two-way communications between far-flung decentralized units and the central headquarters. Failure to do so creates a top management group, isolated from the grass-roots and the powerful customer and the rest of the organization, without adequate control of performance—a double invitation to a disastrous P&L.

Chapter 8

WHATEVER HAPPENED TO
THE GREAT A&P?

> "There is precious little that is unique in
> retailing. You do something and almost
> instantly someone else is doing it with some
> variation. The only thing that counts in the
> end is the performance of management."
>
> William Batten, Chairman
> J.C. Penney

"Let's face it, until fairly recently, the grocery industry hasn't had what you would call aggressive modern management. They were the last to convert from the old entrepreneurial family-run business to professional managers." This comment by the executive director of the National Association of Food Chains fairly represented the state-of-the-art in management throughout the distribution, supermarket, and retailing business until recent years. Most of them have made great strides in improvement. A&P has not!

The Great Atlantic and Pacific Tea Company ("Tea Company" to insiders) has had a very poor image in recent years. Formerly considered a colossal near-monopoly, nemesis of small competitors, and trustbuster target, A&P has come to look like a mangy, toothless old lion. Food sales are no greater than they were ten years ago. Earnings have actually declined in this period. In the ten years prior to 1972 their share of total grocery-chain-store sales

lost nearly 10 percent. The sorry state of management performance can be shown by A&P yardsticks of profitability and
growth as the decade came to a close. Figures are for the
supermarket industry:

	A&P RANK IN INDUSTRY	PERCENT
5 year return on equity	32	3.7
5 year return on total capital	34	3.6
5 year annual sales growth	38	1.4
5 year annual earnings per share growth	38	NEGATIVE

(out of 38 companies)

The reasons for the crisis in management at A&P are varied.
However, most of them can be traced to a bad case of "hardening
of corporate arteries" compounded by serious strategic, organizational, and merchandising shortcomings.

Hardening of corporate arteries

It is not unfair to say that today's top management at A&P,
more than any other major firm in retailing, has suffered from a
bad case of "structural defect inertia." The shadows of the past
have been overwhelming. It is said that if you cut open an A&P
man he'll bleed crimson circles and have the company's slogan,
"Where Economy Rules," engraved on his heart. This heritage of
attitudes and structural defects is still very much with the
company and can be traced back to the waning days of the
Hartfords, who founded and nursed the company to its former
position of prominence. These iron-fisted, old-line managers of the
classical school were John Augustine (Mr. John) Hartford and
George Ludlum (Mr. George) Hartford. Two incidents surrounding
these two pioneers will illustrate how the corporate personality of
A&P emerged in the form that it takes today:

> "Mr. John" was attending a board meeting of the Chrysler
> Corporation in 1951. The subject was the need to bring in young
> blood. John Hartford (age 79) remarked, "Then you won't be

needing me any more." He then stepped into the elevator and died.

In 1957, "Mr. George" Hartford (age 92)—last surviving son of the founder—lay dying. He beckoned sixty-eight-year-old President Ralph Burger to his bedside and whispered his final orders. "Ralph," he said, "take care of the store."

Ralph Burger did take care of the store in much the same way that decades of Hartford rulers had done in the past. Indeed, this carry-over from the past still pervades the company today. Consider an organizational anomaly that illustrates this trait— Ralph Burger. After assuming the duties of Chairman and President, Burger had the responsibility for supervising the company's coffee operations. And, because "Mr. George" couldn't stand the stuff, A&P was woefully and almost disastrously late in entering the instant coffee market.

As we shall see shortly, the company has yet to pull itself up from the attitude that "What was good enough for Mr. John and Mr. George is good enough for us." Archaic, old-line management and merchandising methods of the past were employed right into the seventies. When questioned, the management of A&P resorted to one of two frequently heard clichés: "You can't quarrel with a hundred years of success," or "At this rate, the company will be broke in about two hundred years." Fortunately for this American institution, current management is beginning to change somewhat. Recently, the chairman confessed, "Let's face it, we are a little slow."

Strategy and policies

Right or wrong, A&P's management has been unequivocally clear concerning their strategies and policies. Their concept has usually been, "no change." This attitude has been largely responsible for their lack of growth and profitability.

Product strategy

In its own category—groceries—A&P has been the undisputed champion since early in the century. However, the grocery business has come to mean something much more than groceries alone. While other supermarket operators have long since gone into other, more profitable nonfood items (e.g., drugs, cosmetics, etc.), A&P doggedly stuck to the grocery business. This strategy was expressed by one A&P executive: "There is a higher profit margin on nonfoods, but that's *just not our business.*" Once again we see a holdover from older days when older strategies may have worked. However, the inertia of the past is hard to overcome. The ghost of John Hartford still stalks the halls of management as his philosophy is remembered, "I have always been a volume man. I would rather sell two pounds of butter at a profit of one cent each, than one pound at two cents' profit."

Another questionable strategy is A&P's dogged insistence on promoting its own house brands (e.g., Ann Page) to the detriment of national brands. Despite the fact that house brands account for only 12 percent of sales, this policy has strained relations with major suppliers when A&P's own brands are advertised and given preference in shelf space. As one major supplier of a national brand said, "Sure, we're as mad as hell, but what can we do?" Moreover, this policy loses a lot of customers. When they can't find a famous nationally advertised brand on A&P's shelves (because they were pushing their own), the customers took their business elsewhere.

Growth strategy

Historically, the management of A&P has adopted a passive attitude toward innovations and other policies designed to obtain growth. They have always had a defensive attitude toward such things as broadened product lines, Sunday hours, loss leaders, trading stamps and other promotional devices. This attitude puts the company in the position of allowing competitors to *make policy for it.* Despite the fact that most competitors sell almost 50 percent more per square foot of floor space, A&P has refused to utilize its outlets for many additional kinds of products and services that could be handled at little additional costs.

This historical ultra-conservative approach almost spelled disaster during the depression years of the 1930's when A&P was forced to adopt the supermarket idea. In the early 1960's, while more profitable chains were following the customers to the suburbs and the shopping center, A&P's management was convinced that a depression was just around the corner. They avoided expansion to new stores and opposed long-term leases on the ones they had. While its nearest competitor, Safeway, was moving west of the Mississippi, where the major population and income growth was occurring, A&P was concentrated in the older, more troubled, and relatively stagnant central, southeastern, and eastern metropolitan areas, especially in and around New York. This more aggressive growth strategy by Safeway has resulted in substantially greater growth and profitability than A&P.

The WEO Blunder

In their attempt to salvage a losing strategy, the company decided to go into the discount food business. By late 1972 they had switched all of their 4,200 stores into WEO outlets. WEO was A&P's acronym for *Where Economy Originates*. The result has been near disaster. Sharp price cutting resulted in the biggest, costliest price war in the history of the food industry. In their belated effort to be competitive, A&P touched off a series of events that were partly responsible for an industry profit slide of almost $4 billion. A&P lost over $41 million in six months! Malcolm S. Forbes, Editor-in-Chief of Forbes Magazine, called it " . . . a suicidal spree of price-cutting and overhead increasing that is increasing volume while incurring even huger losses. . . . The whole thing is one of the most incomprehensible major industry capers in the annals of American business."

Organization

Huntington Hartford, grandson of the founder and long-time critic of the way A&P is run, recently commented, "A&P management just feels it doesn't have to listen to anybody. It's the same old story; A&P is mismanaged." Although most people are disinclined to listen to Huntington Hartford's advice because of his own mismanaged affairs (his *Show* magazine flopped, his artists' colony in California faded away, he sold his Paradise Island project at an $18 million loss), his assessment is conceded to have some validity.

The overwhelming majority of A&P executives have never worked anywhere else. Consequently, management is extremely ingrown and virtually self-perpetuating. These qualities make it difficult to do any pruning of personnel or to gain acceptance of new ideas.

A&P is a big monolith built around the notion of profits through careful purchasing—not merchandising. Recently an executive commented, "We were a purchasing organization before we were a merchandising organization—our growth came through purchasing." One result of this policy has been a very strong centralized organization structure that aims at tight control. Although lip service is paid to decentralization, in practice little latitude and initiative is permitted in the field. A frequent result has been just the opposite of what the system was designed to do—centralization has stopped the store manager from obtaining on-the-spot deals that can meet or beat the competition.

In 1969, A&P began a slight move to decentralization—years after other major companies had already accomplished it. Their "big deal" in decentralization consisted of giving 33 regional managers slightly more autonomy. Only recently has the company begun work on a plan to give incentives to store managers—something that other chains had done for over a decade.

In 1968, a new Chairman, William Alldredge, decided to examine the monolithic structure by asking suppliers, regional managers and other executives the question: "What's wrong with A&P?" In his own words, "What they told us about ourselves wasn't flattering."

Management depth

Among old-timers at A&P the organization is known as "the Tea Company." Austerity is the theme. Executives lunch at Schrafft's near the New York Headquarters building. While competitors' stores are gay and decorative, A&P's are unadorned, with bare floors. One gets the pervasive notion that its management must be the same.

Not one of the company's top operating executives has ever come from outside. Even at the store manager level, the president recently bragged, "You never see a help-wanted ad for an A&P store manager." They still like to raise management at home. Yet, despite this promotion from within policy, it might be one of the company's most serious detriments to growth—because A&P's toughest problem is managerial personnel.

The president is frank to admit that recruiting among college graduates has not worked at all. This may be partly due to the image of the company, or it might be due to an old-fashioned idea that a store manager must first be required to stack cans and cut meat before aspiring to a management position.

The time for ingrown management is past. A&P has only to look around in the retailing industry to see that. The time for inter-disciplinary managers is here and it is no longer necessary to be a store manager before rising to the top levels. One need only look to the example of Robert Magowan, an outsider, who took Safeway when it was foundering with a 0.7 percent return, and brought it to within hollering distance of A&P.

Merchandising

One of the first things that every beginning salesman learns in his sales training course is the now-famous slogan of William T. Grants, founder of W.T. Grant's: "Nothing happens until somebody sells something." It is a slogan that A&P might well adopt.

Shrewd buying made A&P the fifth largest U.S. corporation, but its selling strategy can be described as poor, particularly for the 1970's. An A&P executive recently admitted that "we are a buying organization that hasn't learned yet how to sell."

Consider the remarkable statement of Mel Allridge, a recent chairman: "We are in the food business; we don't want to, nor do we need to, promote." This view is in direct contrast with that of another chief executive of a competing and more successful supermarket chain: "We're in whatever it takes to bring them in and sell them."

In today's affluent society, success in the supermarket business turns more and more on merchandising skills and strategies. This axiom, which has brought success to a number of companies, apparently escapes the top management of A&P. Only recently the chairman apologized, "Our coffee cake is as good as Sara Lee's, but the label on their package has a much better design." Despite this admission, there was not even a suggestion that a change is on the way.

Kresge vs. Woolworth: A good guy and a bad

About ten years ago, S.S. Kresge Company was just another old-line variety-store chain that was declining in sales and profitability. They they took the plunge into discounting and became tops in the industry. As one financial analyst said recently, "Kresge is the most dynamic of the large investment quality retailers." At the close of the decade, in 1970, Kresge had risen to be one of the most profitable of the major companies in the retailing industry.

Meanwhile, what was happening at F.W. Woolworth Company? It had slipped from being the giant and the leader in the industry to a position where it isn't in the same league with S.S. Kresge. As its chairman recently remarked, "There was a time when this company could really have fallen out of bed."

Do *management fundamentals* account for the differing track records?

Planning

The dime store business doesn't seem to be a likely place to look for excellent management, but it is just that—characteristic and good decisions resulting from planning—that accounts for Kresge's success. Back in 1959-60 every dime store executive saw that the market was changing; the downtown store was decaying as millions of Americans upgraded their spending. The discounters had carved out a new market for themselves, which lay between the traditional dime store and the typical department store.

Most operators took the narrow view, as did Woolworth: "We'll just move to the suburbs and stay with our old image." The result was a variety chain with a discounting division, and relative *failure*. Kresge, on the other hand, and as a result of extensive planning, concluded that the solution lay in a complete change of company strategy and image to one of becoming a discounter with a variety division. The result was the decision to move into the now-famous K-marts. Today, it has over 400 of them and is a leader in the field. Woolworth is still unsure of its strategy and is struggling to catch up by adopting a "follow the leader" approach.

Control

Retailing's biggest managerial problem is probably cost control. As William Fine, president of New York's Bonwit Teller, concluded, "Control has become a by-word in this business."

Woolworth, like so many dime store and variety store operators, drifted away from their original formula for success: Low margin and high turnover that, in turn, cut the cost of carrying merchandise. They began pricing merchandise on the basis of current costs and sales—not a very good method for controlling costs.

In Kresge's case, cost control became a windfall of their K-mart strategy. By locating K-marts on their own lots, utilizing a standard store design, and licensing 25 percent of the store's departments, they are not only able to get the jump on competitors and saturate cities with *several* K-marts, but they are able to achieve very important economies of scale and standard cost controls that are otherwise not available.

Organization

Perhaps the most important ingredient in Kresge's success has been top management's willingness to innovate and to break with tradition. This, in turn, may have been essential in view of their rapid growth.

First, they admitted that good management was not necessarily a function of long years in the retailing business, but something more was needed. Harry Cunningham, the chief executive who was largely responsible for Kresge's success, startled the industry by speculating, "I think a company of our size needs something more than a former store manager at the top."

Store managers have been given a degree of autonomy that is unusual in the industry. The result has been at least a 25 percent return on investment per store, as managers are allowed to do whatever is necessary to be competitive. Other organizational innovations that are paying off include a policy of refunding money to dissatisfied customers without qualification and broadening their assortments. And to combat the somewhat shoddy image of discounting, store employees are required to be courteous and helpful—qualities not ordinarily found in the competition.

J.C. Penney: How to mind the store
(A case in strategy development)

The top management of A&P, Woolworth, and other lackluster performers in retailing would do well to study the strategy and methods of J.C. Penney's, a company that did a complete turnaround—and found it very successful.

Penney's first store, the Golden Rule Drygoods Store, was established by J.C. Penney in Kemmerer, Wyoming, in 1902. For the following sixty years the strategy of the company remained the same: selling drygoods and staples to lower-middle and lower income families. The name of the company used to bring to mind blue jeans and housedresses. However, and *unlike A&P,* the top management of the company did not rule out change.

In 1957 the then assistant to the president and later chairman, William M. Batten, wrote his now-famous memo on "Company Merchandising Character" to the board of directors. The memo started Penney in a new direction. Batten's constant question became: "What kind of company do we want to be?" The answers to this question caused Penney to turn its back on virtually every policy that had shaped the company since 1902. In ten years Batten took Penney from a drygoods chain, selling little else but staples, to where it is today—one of the greatest transformations ever undertaken by a major U.S. corporation.

Batten and the top management of the company decided that the world was changing and that if Penney hoped to survive, it would have to change also. *Want* had supplanted *need.* Consumer buying patterns were changing; population shifts were occurring; credit had supplanted cash; affluence, penury; fashion, utility.

All of these changes indicated a need for a major strategy departure on the part of Penney's. Management responded. Where it had previously sold only for cash, it now embarked on credit and organized one of the country's largest credit companies. Where it had formerly been a small town retailer, it now became a national, urban and suburban company. Where it formerly was a purveyer of soft goods, it plunged headlong into hard goods. Moreover, it became a full-line merchandiser. It set up an enormous catalogue operation that promises to be second only to Sears. It changed the corporate image from one of staple merchandising to one of fashion–style–youth–leadership. This new image was described by one top executive: "We don't sell shoes; we sell excitement. It really doesn't matter what industry you are in. What counts is how you relate to the customers out there." Penney's relates very well.

All of these things were accomplished at huge cost. But, as Chairman Batten said, "It costs money to change and that cost can be calculated. It also costs money not to change, but that cost cannot be computed." This comment does not reflect a lack of planning. Indeed, this total change was undertaken at great cost and effort in detailed planning at every step along the way. Batten was noted as a careful, thorough, forward planner, who acted only after detailed study. He concluded that after such study, "the decisions just leap out at you."

In summary, Penney's success came as a result of doing *most* of the right things, whereas the relative failure of such slow movers as A&P and Woolworth came from doing *little* of anything and living in the past.

LESSONS TO BE LEARNED

The retail industry has traditionally been viewed as somewhat old fashioned in its management and something less than agressive. This is changing. From the firms achieving progress, and lack of progress, in the industry, we can learn some possible lessons:

Avoid hardening of corporate arteries. Change is constant and the ways of the past are frequently not good enough. Avoid getting into a rut simply because it's the way you've always done it, or because it is comfortable.

Management is a transferable skill. It is not always necessary that managers rise from the ranks in the same company and know every detail of the operation. Consider taking in outsiders if you haven't had the foresight to develop your own bench strength in management.

Review your corporate personality occasionally. Update your strategy. Ask questions like: "What business am I in?" "What kind of company do we want to be?"

Avoid one-man rule. The autocratic leader—however capable—can't be stretched far enough to run today's complex company. Besides, who will replace him?

Don't be afraid of youth. Capability as a manager is not a function of age or experience. Get some tigers in the company.

Don't forget your suppliers. You have a responsibility to suppliers as well as customers (and the government).

Organize for the release of human potential. Don't carry centralization and procedurization too far; you can stifle initiative and innovation.

Keep abreast of change. Yesterday's methods, products, merchandising, and way of corporate life may be out of date for today's world.

Part II
Causes and Cures

Chapter 9

A. T. & T.'S WRONG NUMBER

"The great menace to the life of an industry
is industrial self-complacency."
—David Sarnoff

"Vitality is the power a business generates today that will assure its success and progress tomorrow." These words were written by Frederick R. Kappel, President of AT&T, in 1960. Kappel's book, *Vitality in a Business Enterprise,* was widely acclaimed in business and academic circles as a penetrating analysis of forces of decay that can undermine a currently successful enterprise. It also outlined a program of action to prevent such a decay and to enable the continuation of a healthy, profitable and customer-oriented growth.

In 1965, another AT&T president, B.S. Gilmer, stated that " . . . the ultimate criterion of all we do is service to the public. This is our responsibility and our license to exist. . . . "

By 1969, just a few years later, the telephone service deteriorated drastically, creating widespread criticism of the company's operations and accusations of "the public be damned" attitude on the part of Bell System management.

This rapid reversal and the emergence of immense problems of the previously impeccably managed giant is a significant event in our new industrial society, and a painful proof of the speed of change without a corresponding adjustment by large companies.

American Telephone and Telegraph is our biggest business enterprise. Its 50 billion dollars of assets are 67 percent more than the second ranking BankAmerica Corporation and 158 percent more than the nearest industrial company, the Standard Oil Company of New Jersey. Its annual sales grew at a rate of 8.2 percent during the 1965-1970 period, but the earnings per share increased only at a 2.1 percent rate, and the stock price actually declined 24 percent during that time. See Figure 9-1.

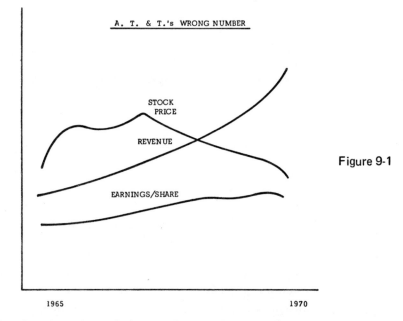

Figure 9-1

The deterioration of the profit margins was the principal cause of the debacle. Faced with continuously increasing costs, the managers, pressed by headquarters, trimmed their budgets over and over. Excessive cost cutting brought about neglect of the "futures," and eventually a decrease in service: inadequate personnel, inadequate maintenance, inadequate equipment in the midst of a major surge in demand.

The good old days

AT&T's basic structure was conceived and implemented by one man, Theodore N. Vail (1845-1921), who was also the first president of the Bell System. Foreseeing a big growth, he instituted a uniquely federalized structure. While the parent company retains large responsibilities and authority, it does allow associate companies to make critical autonomous decisions. The 24 operating companies do their own and separate financing, separate rate negotiations, and have to make individual capital need and expansion decisions. The parent company insists, however, since 1908, that there must be "one system, one policy and universal service."

For some 60 years American Tel & Tel was hailed as "a living proof of the superiority of private ownership and private management—an effective advertisement for private enterprise." Some admirers called it "an adventure in creative thinking and action." The company was growing at a steady rate. It developed superb technology, and the Bell Labs were often the leaders in technical innovations. They produced inventions of great impact, such as the transistor, for instance, and were accepted as practical pioneers in the development of better communication equipment.

The company had well-trained and loyal employees. Its dedication to customer service was genuine, and its actual performance often superb. And above all, the Bell System was well protected from competitors through restrictive tariffs and its own giant size. Thus, the environment was a controlled one. A sense of institutional security and permanence was developed and proudly cherished at all levels of the organization. A tradition, a "Bell culture" was formed, and with it a growth of conformity, an inbred way of thinking, a beginning of overconfidence. The company found it increasingly difficult to respond to change. It began to miss the early warning signals of incipient trouble. A corporate hardening of arteries was setting in.

The New York crisis

During the first 200 days of 1969, the New York State Public Service Commission received more than 4,000 detailed complaints about telephone service—three times as many as in the whole 1968. It was an obvious clue that service was deteriorating at an accelerating pace. Public phones were out of order because of vandalism and insufficient repair crews; businesses had to wait several months for new installations or additional capacity; private phone users were experiencing delayed dial tones, wrong connections, circuit busy signals; exchanges were being overtaxed.

The actual crisis occurred when New York's most modern electronic exchange—the PLaza-8—virtually shut down because of excessive load. After five weeks of serious switchboard troubles, Benton and Bowles, Inc., advertising agency, ran a full-page ad in the *New York Times* of July 14, 1969, somehow sarcastically advising their customers that the agency and its staff—800 strong—were still operating, even if they could not be reached by telephone.

The New York Telephone Company then moved with a little more energy. Fifteen hundred maintenance and service men were "imported" into the city from other Bell companies. Old and recently retired equipment was reactivated to relieve the traffic pressure. New capital expenditures were approved, but obviously no "instant" amelioration or miracle was possible.

How did it all happen? How could a crisis of such magnitude explode without prior concern or knowledge by the experienced telephone company management?

The "numbers racket"

The Bell System loves statistics and has measurements on virtually every element of its services. The New York Telephone Company's goals are high—95 percent service or better must be achieved in all categories. A Manhattan telephone survey showed that:

> 97.5 percent of all calls received a dial tone in three seconds or less.
> 91 percent of Information calls answered within twenty seconds.
> 98 percent of all numbers given out by Information operators were correct.
> 98 percent of all attempts to place a call were effective.

At face value, the above results were certainly satisfactory and would not be normally indicative of an impending crisis. The hidden dangers in such results are true accuracy and "magnitude." It has been said that many reports fed to the higher echelons of management were carefully edited—a polite word for tampered with—to show a good performance. Some internal critics claim that data could have been as much as 40 percent off. This could

happen because promotions and performance ratings are determined how well the quantitative objectives are reached by in-
dividuals and departments. When personal welfare is at stake,
statistical accuracy may often suffer.

The question of "magnitude" is an interesting phenomenon of
our times. Everything is getting bigger and bigger. It has been said,
and rightly so, that our trillion dollar economy is *not* just twice a
500 billion dollar economy; it is a completely new ball of wax.

The New York Telephone Company handles 43 million calls a
day and provides service to some 2.9 million customers. If only 2
percent of calls placed are incorrect or encounter delay or other
troubles, there is a potential of *860,000* frustrated dialers and
complaints daily.

As any businessman knows, a 100 percent perfect service or
quality would obviously cost a prohibitive amount of money, but
if only a 2 percent deviation from the norm creates over 800,000
annoyances daily, is there a practical solution to the problem?
Perhaps the sheer magnitude of the case creates a brand new
situation where prior thinking and experience no longer apply. It
may well be that the overall problem of deteriorating service in the
USA is due to the magnitude of the number of people to be
serviced and requires a completely different approach from the
past.

In September of 1970, AT&T replaced New York Telephone
President Cornelius W. Owens with William M. Ellinghaus. It was
an unprecendented move for AT&T. No operating company
president was ever removed by the Bell before. It was a tacit
admission that a new management was necessary to meet the new
and unforseen challenges of the seventies.

Budget problems

A regulated monopoly with millions of voter-customers is
naturally hesitant to ask for rate increases. Such requests create
public resentment and open many avenues for investigations,
hearings and criticisms. Many a Bell manager preferred during the
sixties to maintain the profit margins and return on investment
ratio through reducing costs rather than applying for higher rates.

Actually the Bell system averaged eleven years of operations without rate increases until the tremendous rush of demands during 1968-1969. Some 790 million dollars of rate increases were requested of state commissions by the AT&T operating companies. The move was necessary to avoid further crisis, but the demands, in times when service was deteriorating and the public was annoyed, did not enhance AT&T's tarnishing image.

The rush for rate increases is not over. During 1970-1971 the Bell System requested an *additional 2.1 billion dollars* of increases. The commissions seem to be granting 76 percent of the demands; thus about 1.6 billion dollars will be added to the $790 million of 1968-1969, making it an approximately $2.4 billion dollar rate increase package in four years.

But the spiral of increases is not over. In 1972, AT&T requested $1,416 million more in rate increases. $811 million were granted. And still $776 million more are being asked. The new president of Mother Bell, Robert D. Lilley, supported by the Chairman, John deButts, is now suggesting a $60 installation charge for a new phone and a monthly limit of five directory assistance calls per customer. Management would like the public to pay through the nose for the declining abilities of Ma Bell's executive suite.

During the years of rate status quo, we had inflation, rising costs, scarcity of labor and fast growth of demand for service. The pressure to cut costs and to operate on lower budgets was felt at all levels of the organization. Bell companies kept cutting corners, narrowing spare capacity—taking inordinate risks with service. In some areas, like New York City, unprecedented surge of demand exhausted already depleted spare capacity reserves ahead of expansion. Service was not only degraded but in some cases collapsed.

The situation was also worsened by continuous skimping on new capital spending. Inflation kept creating bigger capital demands than anticipated, while tight money policy raised interest rates to the highest in history. In effect, capital money dried up when Bell's needs were greatest. The resulting carrying charges were far higher than all the false economy of "savings" effected during the previous years of waiting and skimping.

Forecasting problems

"He who lives by the crystal ball will end up eating ground glass"—purportedly said Confucius. Forecasting has not become any easier in modern times. On the contrary, the rapid change and more complex conditions have turned market and demand forecasting into a "shell game" rather than a scientific practice. Despite all the new techniques and the aid of computers, forecasting at AT&T appears to have been very poor and partially, but not wholly, responsible for the crisis. At New York Telephone, estimates for new service were too low by 22 percent in 1965, too high by 14 percent in 1966, too high by 19 percent in 1967, and too low by 20 percent in 1968.

One of the admitted mistakes was too heavy a reliance on historical trend-line planning, instead of a depth analysis and grass-root survey of the actual market place. It is also hinted that realistic forecasts were not accepted at higher levels of management because they would have in turn generated higher capital demands. Thus, operating companies kept forecasts on the low side and budget cuts on the high side, with disastrous results.

To avoid the repetition of the same situation, the Bell System is planning to prepare future forecasts by four different methods for comparison and better accuracy. It is also becoming apparent to many businesses that the past "fad" of broad macro-forecasting is giving way to elaborate and detailed micro-forecasting, taking into consideration local and regional differences.

People's problems

To manage a work force of 960,000 is a monumental job. To manage it with obsolete techniques is an impossible job.

During the early 1960's, automation and labor productivity kept Bell's manpower within manageable limits of training and efficiency. But the increasing service demand in the second half of the sixties could not be met by technology alone. Large hiring efforts had to be instituted during a period of full employment and a scarcity of skilled labor. AT&T companies experienced a dramatic quality decrease in the caliber of their new hirees. Most of them were untrained and uneducated. As the society became more permissive, the traditional discipline, loyalty and pride of the telephone worker fell to an all-time low. The efficiency of operations suffered accordingly, and the productivity index, measured in terms of employees per 10,000 phones, declined in 1969 for the first time since 1946. The turnover of employees kept climbing. In six years it doubled for operators and quadrupled for craftsmen. Personnel resignations and dismissals varied from city to city, but FCC data indicates that turnover of operators during 1969 was 69 percent in New York, 55 percent in Boston, 40 percent in Los Angeles, and 36 percent for the overall Bell System.

Bell had to interview a million women to hire 125,000, a net gain of only 15,000. The traditional employment practices—regimentation, rules, procedures, coldness and controls—were "turning employees off." Training costs soared as men and women quit soon after completing training—a triple loss of time, money and manpower for the company.

The personnel problem appeared at all levels of the organization. The Bell System breeds its own managers. 147 of 148 officers at Western Electric started their careers with Bell and moved up the ranks. The slow rigid promotion system presents no attraction to new and young talent. The inbred and aging managerial population was unaware and insensitive to the new and changing conditions. They felt secure, comfortable, "bell shaped" and totally unwilling to rock the boat.

Bureaucracy problems

To assure the "one system-one service" policy, Bell attempted to standardize operations by having everything written and explained, to the nth degree of precision. B.S.P.s—Bell System Practices—are super-complete and so voluminous that they defeat their key purpose of effective communication. "Standardization to the point of stultification," and "Forget to suggest anything better, they'll have to change all the manuals," are some of the disillusioned comments about the System. The rigidity of the standardization policy has created an inherent inflexibility and a very slow reaction to change in times when every business is trying to react faster and smarter.

Because of the standardization of practices, inefficient rules degrade service across the nation, in all operating companies. Southern Bell is not an exception. Actually the Miami area was the second worst in service after New York, but the following examples of bureaucracy are universal throughout the system.

A family moved from another state and Bell executed an elaborate phone installation in their new home: two separate lines

and eight extensions. One of the extensions was planned for a
boat dock some one hundred feet away from the house. Everything was completed rather efficiently except for the outside line,
which required digging an underground trench. This was post-
poned for several weeks. The owner started getting complaints
from his out-of-town friends and business associates that they
could not reach him on the phone—the information operator had
no listing for him many weeks after the phones were operative.
An investigation of this situation revealed the following:

(1) All installation work to be done was itemized on one work
order.

(2) Until the work order is completed, no paperwork flows to
any other departments, thus neither information nor billing were
advised that phones were operative.

The obvious solution to anybody with just a little common
sense would be to advise Information the moment any phone in
the house is operative and prepare a different work order for
items still to be completed. But either the B.S.P. or the Southern
Bell did not know how to cope with a very simple problem.

Another ridiculous example of total inflexibility was the
following occurrence with the same unlucky customer. One of his
phones was a regular listing and one was unlisted. By chance, the
unlisted one ended with 3226 and the listed one with 3233. The
Information operator would scan her list down, stop at the first
number, and without another glance announce that she cannot
give the subscriber's number out "at his request." So the
executive was still having troubles with people trying to reach
him, and asked the telephone company why the unlisted number
could not be deleted completely from the Information directory
so as to avoid confusion. This was against Bell practices, he was
told. The reasons were obscure, dealing with billing systems and
people who only had one unlisted number, etc. The rigidity of
the system just does not allow either intelligent exceptions or
improvements to reduce the number of annoyances and legitimate complaints.

Another customer's listing was omitted in the regular yearly
phone book. The reply to the complaint was that the listing was a
convenience only and not an obligation, thus there was no
validity to the complaint. The State Public Service Commission
ruled otherwise. An apology instead of legal mumbo-jumbo
would have made the customer happier and prevented appeals
and frustrations.

At the same time, while claiming that directory listing is a free convenience, the telephone company charges *extra* for not listing your number in the directory. You try to figure out the logic!

Few people would believe that if they have in their homes two separate, regular, listed lines and someone calls Information, the operator is under instructions to only give *one* number out. The customer often has two lines because children keep one phone busy. The Bell's lack of common sense nullifies the advantage of the second line.

But a lot of aggravation and frustration because of deteriorating service is the fault of the apathetic customer himself. While many groups are now being formed to apply pressure and demand corrective actions, they are mainly in locales with extreme crisis situations. The rest of the subscribers are neither militant nor action concerned. Rate increase hearings were recently held in Broward County, Florida, one of the really bad service spots in the country. Broward has over 600,000 residents—eight appeared at the hearing.

Theories vs. realities

Ten years ago, Frederick R. Kappel, then president of AT&T, described his and his company's management philosophy in a series of lectures sponsored jointly by the Columbia Graduate School of business and the McKinsey Foundation for Management Research, Inc.

The key points of his philosophy of management were:

> "The constant responsibility of the head of the business is to do today those things that will build strength for the future."
>
> "A company may be in the full bloom of current prosperity, but dying on the vine as far as its power to build the future is concerned."
>
> "What makes a vital business? Vital *people* make it."

Mr. Kappel also listed several danger signs of loss of vitality that should be detected early, because "by the time the signs are clear and unmistakable, the loss may be so great that recovery is impossible."

These danger signals are greatly relevant to most business enterprises, and particularly to the Bell System. A proper recogni-

tion of such symptoms would have prevented the present crisis at
AT&T. One can only conclude that there is a vast difference
between the theories and philosophies expounded by members of
top management at meetings and in publications, and their actual
practices and actions in running their businesses.

> *Danger Sign I* "People cling to old ways of working after they have
> been confronted by new situations. . . . Clinging to old methods and
> ways of working will not solve the problems that lie ahead of the
> telephone business."
>
> ". . .by innovating we do stand to lose some traditions that have
> had value in the past. But right here is one of the tests of leadership: to
> know the difference between a tradition that is still good, one that
> needs to be modified, and one that should be abandoned altogether."

The Bell System generated through the years its own culture.
Changing conditions had little influence on it. On the contrary,
the impression during the sixties was that of maintaining the
tradition, the managerial philosophy of the past, at almost all
costs. The 26th floor of 195 Broadway in New York City—the
power center of the Bell empire—ignored Danger Sign I.

> *Danger Sign II* ". . .symptom of declining vitality is the failure to
> define new goals that are both meaningful and challenging. . . . The
> fundamental statement of Bell System policy was enunciated more than
> thirty years ago: to provide the best possible service at the lowest cost
> consistent with financial safety and fair treatment of employees."

The trouble with goals that have been in existence for a long
time is that management begins to take them for granted and
employees consider them as nice but superficial platitudes. During
the sixties, Bell management did not change its goals (because they
are still valid) but ignored them in their plans and implementation.
The service declined, the financial safety was endangered, and the
employee morale was seriously damaged and ignored.

> *Danger Sign III* Decline of "reflective thinking as distinguished from
> action thinking." "Reflective thinking covers the mental activity re-
> quired to ask searching (and sometimes embarrassing) questions about
> the adequacy of the current operations."

AT&T's planning for the future was often superb in the years
past. Somehow, during the sixties, and obviously against Kappel's

advice, the company and its affiliates became short-term planners, neglecting the future. The "finger-in-the-dike" philosophy has cost the Bell System its reputation and its profitability.

> *Danger Sign IV* "The growth of institutionalism. . . . In its extreme form, people in the business act as if they believe that the business was always successful and always will be, and that this success is somehow a natural phenomenon that will last forever."

There is no doubt that AT&T is an institution and, instead of fighting the image and its effects, actually was promoting the idea of a stable, successful, prudent enterprise, the "financial darling of widows, orphans and senior citizens." This is not the image that the "new society" wants to see.

> *Danger Sign V* "A business gets the reputation of being a secure and stable outfit, but not a venturesome one."

AT&T's competitors are getting venturesome, and despite Bell's size and power may soon play a major role in the telecommunications industry that up to now was really a rather one-sided affair. Non-Bell communications devices are now allowed to be connected to the telephone network. Private line carriers are emerging. Several satellite systems may be allowed to compete. A greater variety of data and computer services will be offered by various companies since the relaxation of some archaic FCC-Bell regulations. AT&T has to learn how to behave in a growing competitive climate.

> *Danger Sign VI* ". . . danger signal can be seen in the way old wisdom is passed on to new people. Not only do many older managers have the tendency to adhere too rigidly to the ideas, approaches and methods that have produced success in the past, but they also pass this kind of thinking along to young managers."

The personnel departments of Bell's operating companies must have ignored Kappel's advice during the sixties. Turnover of employees soared, hiring became a major problem and the new members of the Bell family laughed at the traditional ways. Many considered Ma Bell as a short stop in their careers, a free training experience. The lack of communications between the old and the new men and women at AT&T was even greater than the often cited generation gap within an individual family.

Danger Sign VII ". . . low tolerance for criticism, with such penalties on thoughtful and responsible critics that criticism is stifled in the whole organization and all independent thinking is discouraged."

The system did not promote self-criticism. The general attitude was, "don't rock the boat." Danger signals were ignored or carefully sugar-coated so as not to upset anyone at any level.

C.W. Owens, the ex-president of the New York Telephone Company (removed from his post after the New York service collapse), was interviewed by Life Magazine in December of 1969. His answers typify the complacency and the "we are always right" attitude of the management. Here are some excerpts:

Q. Mr. Owens, some people have called the situation in New York a crisis or breakdown. Is that how you would describe it?

A. Absolutely not. We've had some pockets of trouble in some critical areas, but that's about all. No question about it.

Q. Have you seen in the past few months where the company made its mistakes?

A. We've gone back in hindsight and asked what we could have done. Finally, we decided that with what we knew then, what we did was right.

Q. You mean this has only been an episode in the company's history and will not recur?

A. Yes. Episode's a very good word.

Q. . . . Have you considered making any other changes in the company's operations in the next few years?

A. I will say that when we get ourselves shaken down this year and next year, we'll be operating just the way we were before. . . . I ask myself if there is something that if I had known two years ago that I know now I would have changed about the company. The answer is no.

P.S. In a subsequent reorganization of the top echelons of A. T. & T. the following promotion was announced. To Executive Vice-President in charge of Corporate Planning and "the applica-

tion of economics and management science to business problems,"
Mr. Cornelius W. Owens, formerly President of New York Telephone Company. No comments are necessary.

Are there lessons to be learned?

The only thing that is permanent is change. No individual, no
institution is immune to its pressures. The Bell System tried to
control change, to mold it to its own timing and logically
developed plans and objectives. But even the world's biggest
enterprise failed to achieve even a modicum of control over the
changing environment and society.

AT&T learned that it must change itself; its policies; its
management style; its once-famous, but now obsolete, "corporate
culture." The corporation tarnished its image—some say irrevoca-
bly—by degrading the quality of its only product, customer
service. It is now trying to regain public support. It will be a costly
and difficult task. Again, just a few short years and a series of
wrong profit vs. service, stockholder vs. customer decisions have
seriously set back a century of corporate progress.

LESSONS TO BE LEARNED

(1) Excessive dependence on past policies, however successful, is
dangerous in time of rapid change.

(2) Excessive pressure on divisions by remote corporate headquarters leads to dangerous, forced decisions (wrong forecasts,
budgets, costs, controls).

(3) Personnel policies must change with the times—often drastically.

(4) Excessive standardization destroys flexibility, dampens creativity and creates uniform mediocrity.

(5) Bigness and success do breed hardening of corporate
arteries.

(6) Never underestimate the power of the irate customer.

Obviously, the giant AT&T will survive its crisis and move
forward again. It is hoped, however, that the experiences of the
Bell System will serve as a constructive and instructional base for
many other firms, small or large. Reforms, policy and operational

changes, and different attitudes and viewpoints are genuinely needed by any type of organization to succeed or even survive in the seventies.

Chapter 10

STRATEGIC PLANNING: IF YOU DON'T KNOW WHERE YOU'RE GOING, ALL ROADS LEAD THERE

We can say beyond any reasonable doubt that a well-directed effort by the top management of an organization can make it grow at a faster rate than the economy in general, and also at a rate faster than the other competitive firms in the industry. The real basis for this effort by top management is organizational *strategy*. Without it, failure is a matter of time.

The development and communication of this *strategy—a unified sense of direction to which all members of the organization can relate*—is perhaps the most important concept in management for top level consideration, and yet it is frequently overlooked or misguided. Unless the organization—its people and its management—have an objective, a corporate identity, a philosophy of what you are in business for, a purpose for existing, and a plan to achieve these objectives, there is no unified direction that management can use to relate day-to-day decisions. Neither is there an organizational environment that fulfills the needs of its members: to employees, the company becomes just a place to go to work.

Without a *strategy* the organization is like a ship without a rudder, going around in circles. It's like a tramp: it has no place to go. And incidentally, such platitudes as "make a profit" or "increase market share" do not provide the *unified direction* we are seeking.

Strategy Development

Like a number of managerial concepts, the notion of *strategy* is taken from the military, where it refers to the science of planning and directing large-scale military operations, the outcome of which may have a significant impact upon whether a war is won or lost. In this context it is distinct from *tactics,* which refers to short-run maneuvers directed to engagement in a single battle. Hence, we have the Strategic Air Command (SAC) with long-range bombers and the Tactical Air Command (TAC) with short-range fighter planes. The analogy for the corporate organization is clear. Many companies are so busy with today's short-run problems—*tactics*—that adequate attention is not given to the longer-run *strategy*. This is bad! It is typical of the mediocre company.

Strategy can be defined as the pattern of objectives, purposes, goals, and major policies and plans for achieving these goals, stated in such a way as to define what business the company is in, or is to be in, and the kind of company it is, or is to be. In other words, *strategy* is concerned principally with organization goals and purpose, and how it deploys its resources to achieve these goals and purposes in reaction to its environment. And quite naturally, since strategy is long-range in nature, its achievement eventually is a function of corporate longevity, and hence profits. Alfred P. Sloan, Jr. stated such a concept succinctly: "The strategic aim of a business is to earn a return on capital, and if in any particular case the return in the long run is not satisfactory, then the deficiency should be corrected or the activity abandoned for a more favorable one."

Strategy is long run

At 5:00 p.m. on a Sunday afternoon, the once mighty Penn Central, with billions in assets, declared bankruptcy. In their short-run rush to become a conglomerate, the management of Penn Central seemed to have forgotten how to run a railraod. The financial drain caused by this departure from *long-run* strategy resulted in collapse.

On the other hand, Union Pacific was able to diversify while maintaining a fundamental strategy committed to the railroad business. The result has been a record of successful operations.

The earlier 1970's brought to an end an era of roller coaster performance for many conglomerates. William Miller of Textron, one of the better performers, concluded that disaster overtook most of them because their philosophy and strategy was "business fundamentals be damned, jazz up the stock and on to the races." Although there was no objection to a strategy of growth through acquisition, the strategic blunder of most conglomerates was to adopt the "growth at any price and in any direction" syndrome. They never stopped to ask such questions as: "What is our corporate purpose?" . . . "What business are we in?" . . . "Where are we headed in the *long run?*"

These illustrations indicate the long-term nature of strategy and the need to make a substantial commitment to it. A number of near failures can be traced directly to short-run thinking for long-run strategy.

Strategy and corporate character

A good strategy that is well-developed will capture the present and projected character of the organization. This, in turn, will go a long way in establishing the unified sense of direction that we seek. (E.g., transportation and not airline, leisure time and not motion pictures.)

The aerospace industry provides us with a number of firms who *did* and *did not* adequately define the nature of their business. Lockheed—"We're in the aerospace business"—lacked a clear definition of their functional product/service strategy. United Aircraft, a company that has had better success, despite recent control problems, developed a product strategy that is much more meaningful—"Our business is energy conversion and the design and manufacture of superior technical products with unexcelled engineering."

A second characteristic of strategy is the definition of market segments. Examples of this are widespread—Lord & Taylor vs. Zayre, *Playboy* vs. *Business Week,* etc.

Using our aerospace industry as the example, once again we see that the relatively successful (for the aerospace industry) United Aircraft has segmented their market along the lines of 50 percent in defense and aerospace, and 50 percent by *selected* diversification into high technology areas with big payoffs. Although United Aircraft suffered a rather classic and severe overrun on their JT9D engine, their basic strategy remained sound. Their future seems more assured than that of their high flying competitors. Lockheed, and Rolls-Royce, on the other hand, have had no clear product policy, and their segmentation of markets appears to be reflected in a philosophy of "Let's get the business wherever we can find it." Hence, we had Lockheed underbidding all competition to obtain a C5A contract, on the gamble that it might later sell in the commercial market.

A good strategy also answers the question: "How will growth be obtained or financed?"

An excellent example of growth strategy is the one adopted by IBM. Realizing that public pressures would not permit them to increase their market share much beyond the 70 percent they enjoyed, Tom Watson concluded that the only way they could grow in the computer market would be to increase the *entire* market and maintain their share of this expansion. This strategy was implemented by education and research—educating computer users in new uses and research into more advanced ways of utilizing the computer. Both of these efforts have paid off by a substantial increase in the total market for computers.

Contrast IBM's strategy with that of the conglomerates. Many of these firms obtained growth through acquisition alone and financed it with "funny money" in an attempt to get something for nothing. Inexorably, the chain letter on this strategy ran out and near disaster resulted.

Finally, strategy should reflect the kind or type of organization that will be built or maintained in order to achieve it.

Complicated though its business is, the principles of organizational life upon which the management of American Telephone and Telegraph (AT&T) is based go back over half a century, to the days of the late Theodore Vail. These two basic organizational principles were simplicity in themselves: (a) concentrate on service, and the profits will take care of themselves, and (b) provide your employees with security, and their loyalty will guarantee service with a smile. Unfortunately for AT&T, things no longer work this way and the organization for the 1930's is not strategically sound for the 1970's—security no longer buys loyalty, because security as such is not so important to employees today.

The result—failure to adjust strategy in accordance with changed organizational needs has seriously jeopardized AT&T's number one product—service!

The company personality

We have argued that the two major advantages to developing strategy are: it gives the company a unified direction to which all members of the organization can relate, and it provides a competitive edge if properly developed and implemented. This is another way of saying that it yields a corporate personality—the individuality that the organization has for its internal members as well as for its various publics outside the firm.

The corporate personality is a valuable attribute. Over the short and near term it is likely to persist largely unchanged even though substantial changes are made in resources and markets.

For decades, A&P has promoted a corporate image based on the characteristics of (a) economy, (b) volume, (c) neighborhood store, and (d) selling groceries only. This personality, which was good for another time and another population, must be reversed if the company is to grow and prosper.

Strategy is pervasive

Because strategy sets the tone for the entire organization, it can and should pervade the company at all levels—another argument for careful development and implementation.

Strategy not only furnishes a guide to action and decision making both horizontally and vertically, it gives us the device we need for achieving synergism in the organization.

A major component of the strategy of Minnesota Mining and Manufacturing (3M) is the vigorous development of international markets. The top level support for such a commitment and the expressed desire that it pervade the entire company was stated by the chairman, Harry Heltzer: "I want to grow an international mentality for the company as a whole. I would like everybody from the top on down to think in terms of what the world requires. The whole world. Not just the U.S. and Europe, but wherever."

The lack of strategy or having the wrong strategy can also be pervasive but in a negative way.

Consider Sperry Rand, the company that pioneered the computer and at one time apparently had a potential stranglehold on the industry. However, procrastination, bad management, internal squabbles, and the *lack of strategy* for developing the market, caused it to fall hopelessly behind IBM, a company that saw an opportunity and developed an outstanding strategy to exploit the market.

Strategy is a prerequisite to planning

There are a variety of schemes for the classification of corporate planning (e.g., time, function, level, purpose, etc.) but none of these can proceed until a foundation of strategy is developed. Moreover, the strategic plan is the primary means to insure that all planning is synergistic . . . , or that everyone is planning against the same premises and with the same goals in mind. This can be shown schematically (Figure 10–1).

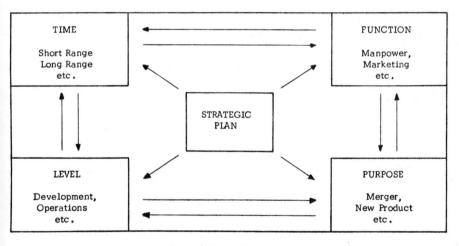

Figure 10-1

In the early 1970's the successful retailing giant, J.C. Penney, developed a two-prong strategy that was quite unique in the industry. This innovative organization adopted a strategy of town planning to implement its merchandising; living and working areas were planned and built around a Penney Center. The rationale was that the former strategy of building a store and hoping that customers will come to the store was too big a gamble. Second, and at the other end of the spectrum, Penney's reversed the trend of abandonment of the inner cities by top corporations and began to prepare for the day when downtown areas will be revitalized.

There has not yet been sufficient time to prove either of these strategies right or wrong. However, the point we want to make here is that such far-reaching decisions have a pervasiveness throughout the organization, and lower level planning must take such strategy into account.

Developing corporate strategy

By studying the successes and failures of the past, we can arrive at two or three generalizations. In the process of formulating company strategy, these suggestions will help:

(1) *Identify Opportunities and Risks*

The end result of this step is the development of market opportunities that may exist now, or in the future, in the environment of the company. After this is done, the task of identifying alternatives and attaching some measure of risk to each can be accomplished; this process yields an array of alternatives that the company *might* undertake, and the choice depends upon the degree of risk it is willing to accept. Presumably, this degree of risk is a function of the profit objective.

> The computer industry provides a good example of how opportunities and risks were assessed by a number of companies and what went wrong. General Electric and RCA are among those who gambled and lost enormous sums on the road to getting *into* and *out of* the computer business. On the other hand, TRW (whose strategy was to compete only in lines that are profitable, and in which they were knowledgeable) was able to forecast potential failure and sell out before losses piled up.

(2) *Appraise Company Strengths and Weaknesses*

After identifying opportunities and risks, the company has, in effect, determined what it *might* do. The second step in strategy formulation involves a determination of what it *can do* in terms of its strengths, weaknesses, competences, and resources. Some kind of equilibrium must be obtained from what sometimes appears to be opposing forces. The result of this process is frequently called the company's *economic* strategy: a statement, of course, of action after an appraisal of its actual or potential capacity to take advantage of what it believes to be market opportunities and risks.

> As a group, the conglomerates have fallen fast and far. *Forbes* concluded, "The conglomerates are now deemed a disaster area and the good has been written off with the bad. And written off not only as troubled, but somehow as morally reprehensible." The interesting question arises as to whether these companies adequately appraised their strengths and weaknesses in their acquisition binges and whether their strategy of "acquisition for its own sake" was adequately developed.

(3) *Reconcile Strategy with Personal Values and Corporate Obligations*

After an economic strategy has been determined, the difficult step of reconciling it with personal values is attempted. These values may be those of the owners, the chief executive, or other top management groups. Frequently, these values lead in quite a different direction from the economic facts of life. Nevertheless, some reconciliation must be made. The business world is replete with examples of corporate strategies that have been influenced in this way: Tom Watson of IBM, Joseph Wilson of Xerox, Alfred Sloan of General Motors, Harold Geneen of IT&T, to name but a few.

> In the early and middle sixties, evidence seemed to favor a three-part market strategy for Chrysler: a small car, an entry in the foreign market, and diversification to avoid the 95 percent dependence on auto sales. However, under Lynn Townsend, Chrysler moved with too little commitment and also too late with their modified strategy. Were personal values involved?

Another element with which strategy must be reconciled is that of *corporate obligations and responsibilities* to persons and groups other than the stockholders. This consideration is accelerating and growing rapidly in importance, and it becomes more necessary for corporations to adopt values other than the profit motive.

> Bethlehem Steel reports that pollution abatement will cost them about $500 million and an additional $45 million in annual operating costs. The reduced flexibility resulting from this type

of involvement was mirrored in a statement of the company president, "Our philosophy used to be: Stay out of the press and stay out of Washington, but you can't stay out today just because you don't like the rules. The steel industry is finding it must frequently play by the other fellow's rules."

LESSONS TO BE LEARNED

(1) Develop a strategy. Put it in writing. Be specific—be precise. Don't hedge—don't use "public relations"-type statements.

(2) Make it a number one priority effort. Don't spare talent, time and resources to develop a viable strategy. Your company's future depends on it.

(3) Don't place short-term expediency before long-term growth or survival. Don't "damn the fundamentals to jazz up the stock."

(4) A strategy requires total management commitment. You have to live it—lip service strategy is worse than none, because it lulls management into a false sense of security.

(5) A strategy development must cover all phases of future action. Neglect or superficial treatment of financing, market definition or organizational structure, for instance, will jeopardize the company's future. Implementation of a good but incomplete strategy may be as disastrous as a completely erroneous one.

(6) Don't stick stubbornly to your strategy when the times change or unforeseen events make it obsolete. The success of a past strategy is no assurance of its automatic continuance. Check and recheck the clues of change.

(7) Don't hide your strategy under a bushel. Communicate it throughout your company. Make it all. pervasive and let it set a tone and a character to your organization. It's better today to disclose too much than too little.

(8) Don't start operational planning, five-year planning, long- or short-range planning—any planning—without first defining, stating and explaining your strategy. It's the all-important foundation to planning and allocating your resources.

Chapter 11

OPERATIONAL PLANNING: HOW TO GET WHERE YOU'RE GOING

"Get the facts. Explore alternatives. Make the detailed study. Plan. After that, the decisions just leap out at you."
William M. Batten, Chairman
J.C. Penney

New strategies often appear to be exciting. Changes in corporate direction and proposed organizational innovations usually promise better growth, better profitability—better "everything." For this reason these changes are often presented with enthusiasm. Accompany this enthusiasm with caution, however, because strategic changes require the down-to-earth preparation of detailed operational plans for achievement of new objectives.

The tactical or operational plan for achieving a strategic change must be practical, because the future of the company may hang in the balance. The classical steps of setting objectives, preparing a work plan, then implementing and controlling progress and results, is still valid and all important. Neglecting any one of these steps can result in disaster, as many corporate giants have found.

The most common error is the hurried leap from strategy development to implementation without the all-important intermediate step of *operational planning.*

Operational planning and the Volkswagen incident

Sometime during the mid-sixties, the top management of Volkswagen decided that after 25 years of turning out the same basic car—the beetle—it was time to change. The "beetle" had begun to lose its appeal. Perhaps a broadened product line was needed. Thus emerged the new strategy to make Volkswagen into a multimodel-multidivision company patterned after Detroit. Elements of the strategy included:

(1) Entry into the medium and luxury car field through acquisition of Auto Union and NSU, thereby forming the Audi-NSU Division.

(2) Technical innovation represented by the introduction of the Wankel rotary engine on the expensive NSU, R-80 model.

(3) Expansion of the basic Volkswagen "beetle" line by the introduction of the 1302 "super beetle" and the 411 sedan.

(4) Modification of all lines of Volkswagen to conform to U.S. safety standards.

The strategy appeared sound, well-conceived, and even conservative. There were no wild diversifications, no disruptive organizational changes, no great unknowns, no risky gambles. On the surface everything looked like the progressive evolution and expansion of a very prosperous and efficient business. And yet the implementation of the strategy became a nightmare and almost spelled disaster for Volkswagen. It also meant the loss of a job to Kurt Lotz, VW's iron-handed chairman. Additional costly results included:

> The Audi-NSU became a big money loser. Volkswagen, a company that excelled in producing and marketing a single style low-priced car, did not really know how to sell medium- and luxury-priced automobiles.
>
> The "revolutionary" Wankel engine on the expensive R-80 NSU model was not adequately engineered. Its malfunctions, together with the cost of replacement parts, cost millions of dollars above the planned budget.
>
> The "new look" Volkswagens were late, costly and full of bugs. The 411 sedan is said to have been named "411" because it

had 4 doors and was introduced 11 years too late. Over 200,000 of the new VW 1302 "Super Beetles" were recalled because of a variety of potentially dangerous mechanical faults.

The popular and apparently superbly "debugged" beetle itself became a target of attack. Ralph Nader's Center for Auto Safety charged, in a 200-page report, that the beetle "is the most hazardous car in use in significant numbers in the U.S." VW must have recognized that problem before Nader did, because its investment outlays soared some $250 million above their previous year's norm, most of it required to meet present and future safety requirements.

Volkswagen did not raise its prices in step with the new currency values caused by revaluation of the German mark. It was "locked in" to existing prices because it was facing formidable competition from both Japan and Detroit. Even *Consumer Reports,* the magazine that was a perennial advocate of the small car in general, and VW in particular, gave the Volkswagen lower marks in comfort and performance than several of its competitors. Long years of unchallenged market dominance may have dulled VW's competitive edge and infused a false and complacent feeling of security.

What does it all mean? What went wrong with VW's operational planning in pursuit of an apparently sound strategy? Was the strategy ill-conceived in the first place? Probably not. Could it be, on the other hand, that the implementation of a sound strategy and a well-developed operational plan failed because of a lack of controls and slow reaction to unforeseen problems and circumstances?

Using Volkswagen and other companies as illustrations, let's examine some DO's and DON'T's about how to perform the *operational planning* process in the implementation of a strategy.

Don't try to copy methods in unlike products

The most successful method of operation in one business market or product will not necessarily show the same results when adapted to another kind of operation.

A low-price car business is much different than one in the luxury class. GM doesn't operate Cadillac in a Chevrolet manner.

VW tried to apply successful VW principles to the Audi-NSU operation—with disastrous results.

While most dime store operators and variety-store chains were moving to the suburbs and upgrading their image for more affluent markets in the sixties, F.W. Woolworth tried to invade the market by staying with their old central city dime store image. The result was that Woolworth's is still trying to catch up with their competitors, whose strategies were implemented better with appropriate operational planning.

Don't rush a revolutionary technical innovation to the market

Do not rush a revolutionary technical innovation to the market without testing, retesting, and testing again. The marketing people will usually push for early introduction by promising huge sales results or threatening competitive inroads. Top management becomes seduced by engineering, pre-production models that operate beautifully during a few-minute demonstration. The market research charts forecast share of the market gains that are irresistible. Prudent management and proper caution are thrown to the winds, giving way to "entrepreneurial risk" and a "super growth" syndrome.

Audi-NSU did not have the rotary Wankel engine ready for mass production and tough road use. The Japanese did. In fact, the Toyo Kogyo Company of Japan, having paid $12 million to Audi-NSU in the early 60's for Wankel rights, spent over seven years and $20 million improving the engine, far above the Germans. The result is that U.S. manufacturers are negotiating for rights with the Japanese rather than with the original developers.

The Rolls-Royce bankruptcy resulted from a similar situation. Rolls' marketing people and the chairman, Sir Denning Pearson, were obsessed with growth at any cost. They wanted to crack the U.S. market by winning the contract to supply the Lockheed L-1011 Airbus engine. The plans for the RB. 211 engine were so completely unrealistic that one wonders how any management could have so completely ignored fundamental cautions in promising such advances in technical innovation in such a short time and at such a bargain price.

The development cost of $156 million became $180 million, then $324 million. Shortly before bankruptcy, it was up to $408 million—2-½ times the original figure. If you were to add the potential additional losses on the production costs and the late delivery penalties, Rolls-Royce losses would have added to almost a billion dollars on a sale of 540 jet engines. This would have dwarfed the debacles of General Dynamics' Convair, the Ford's Edsel, RCA's EDP and DuPont's Corfam combined.

Don't shortcut quality

What is more, whatever plans you have to produce a product within your approved quality standards, *raise* your specifications. Assume that you are going to have unparalleled production and quality problems even with products that you know well, after having produced similar ones for years and years. These actions will help keep you on the safe side of quality.

Today's society is complex and full of surprises. Employees take less pride in their work, and their loyalties to the organization or to the plant are diminishing or disappearing. The trend to decentralization reduces overall controls and often disastrous conditions can begin, and continue in remote locations without top management's awareness. This is not the place to discuss the socio-economic and psychological reasons for the above trends, but the pragmatic fact of life is that the condition exists. Service and quality workmanship are rapidly deteriorating.

Acknowledging this situation (as hard to swallow as it may be to a chief executive), operational plans must provide higher contingencies for "unks unks" (Lockheed's term for unknown unknowns). If you had reserves for faulty materials, faulty assembly, errors in production and careless handling in transit, *double* or *triple* these reserves to be on the safe side. Then try to correct the situation. But don't close your eyes as many giants have done.

After 25 years of the most careful planning of operations and stressing quality, VW assembly faults cost the company a large percentage of their dwindling profits.

Testimony before Congressional Committee revealed examples of gross carelessness and waste at the Lockheed plants. When 42 tons of steel are left exposed to the elements at a cost of hundreds of thousands of dollars, it is a symptom of a "who cares?" syndrome, to say nothing of deteriorating quality control. The rationalization of Lockheed's executive vice president, H. Lee Poore, "We are only people ... We are not perfect," will not improve the firm's P and L statement. Lockheed's losses of some $480 million on four defense projects cannot all be blamed on "unks unks." Operational planning that does *not* consider inflationary trends, supply shortages, engineering changes, design errors and learning curves is *not* planning. The factors cited are not really *unknowns.* They are present in any project at any time. Proper contingencies and reserves must be included in the total cost. estimates. If inclusion of such reserves makes the project *unprofitable,* don't bid on it; don't produce it; forget it! Forgetting or omitting expensive but realistic contingency plans is hiding one's head in the sand. The outcome of such behavior is obviously disastrous. How such simple fundamentals can be ignored is puzzling, but nevertheless it's not an isolated case.

Don't overlook the public

Operational plans must include provisions for complying with the changing demands of society, the public at large, the government, and the specific customer. This part of planning will be covered in greater detail in the chapter discussing the ninth commandment of management: "Don't overlook the customer and the customer's new power." It is important to stress, however, under this discussion of operational planning, that ignoring a trend, particularly a disagreeable one, is not going to make it disappear.

Volkswagen is spending millions of dollars in a crash program to adapt its cars to U.S. safety regulations. These regulations did not appear overnight. The trend toward automobile safety and more rigid governmental regulations has evolved over a period of many years. It is true that it has accelerated, but this is, and will be, the case with any present or future trend in our society. There will be a significant compression of time for obtaining results faster. Thus, plans must foresee and account for a more rapid compliance, as well as higher costs with any sociological trend that may affect business. Existing trends include customers' and employees' safety, early retirement, sabbaticals, pollution control, landscape beautification, industrial traffic, architectural and zoning restrictions, minority training and employment, to name just a few. To ignore these is a reflection of the ostrich syndrome—refusing to look at simple fundamentals.

The DuPont Company is being revitalized. A non-member of the DuPont family is running the firm for the first time in more than 170 years. Realizing that the pressure for air and water pollution control is not going to abate, President and Chairman Charles B. McCoy announced that the company will be spending *$100 million a year* for installing and operating pollution control devices. The magnitude of this move and perhaps its lateness is demonstrated by the fact that the total DuPont investment in pollution control to date was only about $168 million, or less than 5 percent of assets.

Union Carbide was called "one of the nation's worst corporate polluters." Exposés of indiscriminate polluting by Carbide plants in Ohio and West Virginia precipitated a major top management change (already brewing because of a five-year slump in profit margins). Carbide's chairman, chief executive officer and his vice-chairman took "early retirements" and a new chief executive stepped in. Pollution control spending is being doubled and is approaching $50 million annually. Obviously, plans for the future *must* include an even larger amount because of society's pressure.

Public health and safety is becoming an increasingly important concern and covers fields undreamed of just a few years ago. In some cases, plans may backfire when a company tries to take a positive step and exploit a trend without proper research in depth.

W. R. Grace built a 60 million-pound-capacity domestic plant for the production of NTA (nitrilotriacetic acid). This was a chemical substitute for phosphates in detergents, which were temporarily banned by the government and independently boycotted by a segment of the public because of their polluting effects on the rivers and aquatic life. The government, in turn, banned NTA, pending further study, because of the direct health hazard to the housewife using the new detergent. Grace had to take a $2.9 million write-off to shut down a substantial part of its NTA production capacity. Doesn't it seem obvious that a company would check the toxicity of a new product designed to replace one that was banned because of its toxicity?

Competition cannot be underestimated

Complacency concerning competition on the part of the leader will lead to rapid downfall. On the other hand, a number two in an industry cannot bridge the gap by just copying the leader or trying to compete on the basis of price cutting. This conclusion seems so self-evident that one feels apologetic to inflict upon the reader a "firm grasp of the obvious." Yet many corporate giants have fared poorly by ignoring such simple fundamentals.

The powerful Volkswagen company ignored the Japanese Toyotas and Datsuns and smugly dismissed the first Pintos, Vegas, and Gremlins from Detroit. But the Japanese do not give up easily. After their original debacle in the early 60's, they came back strong. Good quality, an extensive dealer and service network, appealing design, and competitive price contributed to a rapid inroad on the VW's U.S. share of the market. VW is no longer smug or complacent, but their cost of learning fundamentals will be high.

RCA's decision to abandon the computer field after two decades of trying is a classical example of a dogged determination to succeed with non-innovative, "me too"-type plans. The end of the road was paved with a minimum of $250 million in red ink—the total loss being closer to half a billion dollars—and layoffs that may affect as many as 10,000 employees. The paradox of the situation is that IBM, already in the midst of major anti-trust litigation, may gain additional customers and revenue and increase its share of the market. This is not what the undisputed leader in the computer field really wants or needs, as it only increases its hazards to additional anti-trust actions.

RCA plans were to make "Chinese copies" of IBM systems and to *under*-price the industry leader, who always maintained a "price umbrella" over its original seven dwarfs (GE, RCA, Univac, Honeywell, Burroughs, CDC and NCR). With GE and RCA gone, but with the weak entry of XDS (Xerox Data Systems), there are now only six dwarfs and none of them too healthy.

The fundamentals are again simple: When you imitate the leader and operate on a price differential only, you are never in control of your own destiny. You are entirely dependent and at the mercy of the leader's moves. Any new product introduction or price change can throw you to the canvas, usually for the count.

Another lesson learned from the RCA-IBM battle is that mass hiring of a competitor's personnel is usually not very successful. A company cannot really offer major financial and salary advantages to people being already paid at the high scale of the industry norm. Psychologically, satisfied employees prefer to stay with a winner. "When you're with a winning team, who wants to be traded?" said once an IBM executive when offered a job with a competitor. Thus, a distant second usually hires away malcontents, hangers-on, and men who do not see any future for their jobs—in short, people the leader would be glad to release. This is not the sort of team to start winning, or even bridging the gap between approximately a 75 percent and 4 percent share of the market.

LESSONS TO BE LEARNED

Many costly mistakes are made by seemingly successful corporations and talented executives. Most of these mistakes could be avoided by paying diligent attention to simple fundamentals and business textbook precepts.

In the case of operational planning, remember the third commandment of business:

> "Plan your operations realistically—
> Pay attention to details and do not
>   omit contingencies for unknowns."

Particularly, do not ignore some obvious advice:

(a) Don't apply proven and successful methods and means of your key business to another one you either started or acquired. Each business needs its own custom-made plans.

(b) Don't rush technology. Prototypes look good, but they don't become production models overnight. Pushing too-hard unknown technical problems for early solution will double or triple your costs and lose you customers, or even the business.

(c) Don't sacrifice quality. Don't trust your quality control. Double it to maintain it at the level of the past, because quality-mindedness is on the decline.

(d) Don't ignore the changes in the society and the environment. Don't fight the public; you are bound to lose. Prepare for the future demands of the public and the government by doubling your efforts now.

Chapter 12

CONTROLS: DELEGATION DOESN'T MEAN ABDICATION

Item. After investing $21 million in Executive Jet Aviation, Inc., Penn Central was found to be illegally in control of an airline by the Civil Aeronautics Board. Further, the holdings are worth less than $1 million and legal action has been taken against "inside" operations.

Item. Diner's Club lost over $70 million in two years as a result of losing control of credit card processing expense and associated fraud, as well as competitive forces.

Item. 40 cost control specialists from the U.S. Navy are seeking ways to control cost overruns on the F-14 airplane at Grumman.

Item. The longtime failure of the management of General Dynamics to bring the company under control threatens serious and permanent harm. Their reputation has suffered badly among the armed forces and the company has not won a major contract in a decade.

Item. Losing ventures in computers, nuclear power, and jet engines have cost General Electric more than $500 million in after-tax profits.

Item. Troubled Chrysler Corporation tries everything to get costs under control. Their latest effort involves major organizational changes. The tight operational controls that had characterized Lynn Townsend's reign suddenly slackened. Overnight, Chrysler's profits plummeted, and many of the company's gains were obliterated, (1968-1970).

It may be stating the obvious to say it, but no plan, no objective, no result can be achieved unless the organization and its operations are brought under control. Many spectacular failures could have been avoided if managers had paid more attention to the fundamental process of management, *control.*

Cost control: management by panic

The economy slows; sales slacken; budgets must be cut. Cost-cutting announcements are a daily item in the business press. Electronic firms trim their work force by 20 percent. Faced with tight money, utilities eliminate marketing plans. Advertising budgets are slashed. An airline announces a major executive shake-down. College recruiting is off by half.

For the public consumption, moves such as these are usually labeled "readjustments." But, at best, cost-cutting actions such as these are evidence of the failure of—or lack of—planning. At worst, it is indicative of "panic management," an affliction that affects many corporations, particularly those that fail to establish good programs of planning and control.

For companies that practice "panic management," cost cuts are characterized by the fact that they are usually sudden, one-shot affairs and can hit any segment of the company. This approach can do irreparable damage to personal relationships, established systems, and employee attitudes. It is a sure sign of mismanagement. Here are some typical one-shot actions and the results that can be expected:

ACTION	RESULT
Operational change (e.g., reduce reject rate and use cheaper fabrication materials)	Increased consumerism. Reduced customer good will.
Replace secretaries with office typing pool.	Resentment and slowdown by remaining employees.
Moratorium on advertising.	Rob next year's sales.
Replace labor with equipment.	Remaining labor beats hell out of the equipment.
Layoff	Long-term damage to community relations.

Too little with too late at Litton

Litton Industries provides a good example of how a great corporation can get out of control and take the wrong actions to recover. Despite the fact that Litton had, in theory, one of the best control systems in the country, it failed to work properly for reasons we will outline later in this chapter.

After fourteen years of unbroken growth, Litton finally began to suffer in 1968 from growth pains accompanied by indigestion from its many acquisitions. The organization became so complex that tight control was almost impossible. When profits and stock prices slipped, panic set in. The word went out to the divisions to cut cost and lay off people. However, these remote orders from financial headquarters took little account of the nature of the business or the people involved. In their publishing division, Van Nostrand-Reinhold, long-time operating managers and editors were summarily fired in apparent ignorance of the nature of the publishing business, which requires continuity unlike that of aerospace or manufacturing.

In their panic to cut costs, other divisions became trapped in the three-way cycle: increased costs, followed by higher selling prices, that are in turn followed by reduced sales. In the office products division, prices were raised an average of 28 percent to compensate for increased labor and material costs. These higher prices seriously affected sales, and the reduced volume pushed unit costs up still further. Little action was taken to achieve a profitable sales level at the higher prices. Panic cost cutting was expected to take care of it.

Profit planning

Profitability is the ultimate test of management effectiveness. It measures how efficiently management is using the assets entrusted to it. This efficiency is the end result and the reason for profit planning. Moreover, growth—a co-equal with profitability—is normally a function of how well management plans its profits and achieves them through proper control.

Firms in the aerospace industry are notoriously poor at profit planning and control. Cost overruns at Lockheed are now legendary and almost resulted in the bankruptcy of this troubled plane maker. And yet, despite the incredible lack of control on the C5A airbus, one of Lockheed's divisions (Lockheed Missiles & Space) is noted as having the best control system in the business. Perhaps the parent should have taken a lesson from the child.

Despite the lessons learned from the $250 million Convair debacle, General Dynamics continues on its path of seat-of-the-pants planning and control. In one year alone over $40 million was lost on shipbuilding due to the poor estimating and subsequent control of costs on a fixed price contract. Even Litton, with its famous system of tight controls, fell prey to the cost-plus syndrome in its shipbuilding effort for the government. Litton's management admitted that it was only after they got into the commercial shipbuilding business that any real means of cost control was developed.

DuPont: A case of good profit planning

Although this great American company, whose name is a household word, has had its recent troubles (e.g., industry overcapacity, $100 million loss on Corfam, loss of market share), it remains one of the most profitable (14 percent return on investment) in the industry. This relative standing can be traced directly to the company's system of profit planning and control. Indeed, DuPont has been a pioneer in financial management for years, and other companies around the world have benefited from their efforts.

The secret of DuPont's system lies in its simplicity and, hence, its effectiveness. Essentially, it consists of identifying those elements in the cost-profit equation, establishing targets and standards of performance for these elements, and following up on the financial/profit plan with proper control measures.

Pitfalls in profit centers

Delegation and decentralization were the great management fads in the sixties. Organizations struggled to decentralize operations and delegate decisions to the lowest possible level. The natural organizational device to facilitate this movement was the *profit center*. Under this concept the responsibility for profit was delegated to the manager concerned and he, in turn, was compensated on how well he achieved his profitability target.

The danger in the profit center scheme, or any format where the manager's compensation is tied to a profit formula, is the temptation for a quick earn-out at the cost of company goals. After all, profit isn't the *only* objective. When performance is measured by profits alone, the "creative bookkeeper"-type of manager can really fool you if he wants to. It is also a natural tendency of an operating man to be a squirrel and approach the profit planning/budgeting process with the idea of putting away chestnuts so that he can come up with big increases at the end of the year.

Overall controls

Cost controls are essential, but more is needed.

The General Electric gamble

For years, and during most of the 1960's, General Electric had the reputation of being the best-managed company in the United States. They did all the right things and operated the company according to textbook management principles. Their traditional lines of industrial and consumer products were profitable, and the company grew under carefully planned and controlled programs. Then came diversification into high-technology industries and enormous losses piled up—over $400 million in computers alone.

Although a number of lessons can be drawn from GE's recent record, it appears that the major one is this: *control of operations is not enough—overall controls are required.*

The Litton lesson

Sunday afternoon, January 21, 1968, marked the end of an era for American business. On that afternoon, five of Litton's top officers (including chairman Charles Thornton and president Roy Ash) were meeting in their Beverly Hills headquarters to decide how to tell the world that Litton was in trouble. For the first time in its fourteen-year history, the company was anticipating a quarterly decline in earnings. This event marked the first in a series of very serious declines in Litton's growth and profitability, and started the beginning of the end for the conglomerate movement.

The picture that emerged shortly thereafter showed repeated and seemingly elementary mistakes in production, cost estimating, pricing, and marketing. Litton's famous system of internal fore-casting and communication had a breakdown. Management had failed to detect in advance the seriousness of problems that had grown in a number of divisions.

The situation at Litton was particularly incongruous in view of their management group. The men who ran the company probably formed as brilliant a crew as could be found in any corporation in the world. Their computer-based management information system was so famous, and presumably efficient, that President Nixon appointed Ash to head up a committee to recommend a similar system for the federal government. Their control system mea-sured each month the detailed performance of each division against plans and projections.

In view of all this, the question is asked: How did things get out of control? The answer probably lies in the lack of *overall controls*. Although operating controls appeared to be sufficient, the overall control of the company was lost because major issues, organizational entities, projects, and business sectors were not sufficiently accounted for. Litton's system of constant, micro-scopic checking of the performance of its divisions were designed to quickly correct errors at lower levels. But what about at the top level? Indeed, in a subsequent report to stockholders, "earlier deficiencies of management personnel" was blamed on losses. Perhaps also, they "couldn't see the forest for the trees."

Another go-go conglomerate that had a fine system of *oper-ational* controls but lacked *overall* controls is Whittaker Corpora-tion. This once fast-stepping California company convinced Wall Street that they had married technical prowess with managerial acumen. On paper, their operating controls looked good enough to be foolproof. Their seventy-odd divisions were visited by a group executive each month, and division managers were required to submit detailed monthly reports to headquarters. Each division manager was required to periodically defend his performance against a plan and a budget.

Despite these controls, profits took a nosedive and the stock price tumbled from 47 to 5. The problem was in *overall* controls. Examples: It was discovered that eight different divisions, simultaneously and unknown to each other, were working on the possibility of developing urethene. The vice-president of R&D was unable to break out the amount spent on internal R&D as opposed to the amount spent on R&D for the government. Another division spent $3.2 million to automate a line, then spent another $3 million for reworking the products that came off the line. Then, closing the management loop, quality control was lowered in an effort to boost profits. But the effect was to reduce sales and cause another boost in unit costs. Management, 2,000 miles away in Beverly Hills, was unaware before it was too late. Like many conglomerates, Whittaker came *too far too fast.*

Qualitative controls

For the first time in the fifty year history of the famed DuPont executive committee, the members (nine vice-presidents) have recently been assigned "liaison" duties over the twelve operating departments. Historically, this committee has had no direct-line authority over the operating departments. They could only give orders to their secretaries. The clear intent of the new organizational change is to keep top management in closer touch with the shorter-range business problems of operating management. It was found that the famed DuPont system of controls was not automatic, nor did it cover the many areas that required *qualitative* control standards. As one of the managers of an operating division put it: "We have not done well in recent history. This is a fact of life. The question is, 'Do we understand why we haven't done well?' " Clearly, there is a recognized need to have control over other standards of performance than the quantitative ones.

Litton's poor performance can be traced directly to the nature of their control system. In theory, their system of management control should have revealed problems long before they occurred. Their microscopic checking of performance over predetermined standards was textbook perfect. However, there are inherent limitations to the amount of control that any company can exercise over its operations. One of Litton's operating vice-presidents admitted that top management was not getting the right information. He said: "Litton has very fine *quantitative* reporting techniques, but not qualitative. They must rely on their divisional managers to tell them that they are taking care of things qualitatively—whether they are keeping up with the field, with their customers' needs, with technology."

TRW, another conglomerate that has had relative success by comparison, does have qualitative controls. TRW executives insist that what happened to Litton couldn't happen to them. Their reasons include:

(1) a strict reporting procedure that puts every division manager on the carpet once a month;
(2) strict insistence on accurate projections; and
(3) a mandatory formality that makes the best advice in the company accessible to everyone.

Indeed, TRW attributes their success with controls to the informal cross-flow of information below the top management level and *with* the top management level to be the secret of their qualitative approach to control. This informal approach includes review sessions among peers and a company-wide policy of open door access to top management.

A large part of the failure on the part of the conglomerates and other expanding companies to control growth can be attributed to the lack of qualitative controls. Most companies simply expanded an existing system of budgeting to include additional acquisitions or products. Others attempted to couple this with a "free form" style of management (Whittaker) or other various devices (e.g., profit center) for delegation in an attempt to reduce the need for strict control. However, it is now clear to all that whatever the management innovation, it must be accompanied with both *quantitative* and *qualitative* control systems.

Overcontrol and paperwork

A final caution should be made regarding control: the tendency is to *overcontrol.* If managers pay lip service to control or if they are innundated with paperwork, then control becomes the tail that wags the management dog. In other words, control and the associated paperwork become the ends instead of the means. Or worse yet, people view it as a distasteful job to get done without regard to its value as a management tool.

The Federal Government is famous for red tape, paperwork, and overcontrol. Former Assistant Secretary of Defense Packard said that in some government contracts paperwork accounted for more than 30 percent of the cost of the contract. The president of Whittaker Corporation made this frustrating conclusion: "We have a couple of divisions that can't go to the bathroom without government permission." On the other hand, not all red tape and bureaucracy is found in the government. Unless used for the purposes intended, and unless reviewed periodically, any control system stands a good chance of reverting to mere bothersome paperwork. Many employees of the Bell System feel this way about the famous Bell System Practices—called "BSP's" by most insiders. Such a system is so structured, so rigid, that it stands in danger of stifling initiative—a condition said to exist in the Bell System at the present time.

LESSONS TO BE LEARNED

Judging from operational successes and failures, control warnings should include these:

Avoid panic cost cutting. At best, indiscriminate cost cutting is an admission that previous operations were too fat. At worst, the practice will cost you more in the long run than the short-term savings that accrue.

A control system is not automatic. A well-designed system with the best procedures won't work without attention. People—not paper—make it work.

Profits don't just happen—they must be planned. A good profit planning and control system (budget) lies at the heart of profitable operations. And don't just pay lip service to profit planning and control; make it for real.

Be wary of profit center. The concept is an excellent one for control of operations, but make sure that the profit center manager isn't a "creative bookkeeper" and that he is aware of company goals other than short-term profit.

Cost controls aren't enough—overall controls are needed. These are related to your progress toward other resources, such as customers, suppliers, government, plant, strategy, employees, managerial development, growth, quality control, service, competition, etc.

Qualitative controls are as important as quantitative. Go behind the figures and measure the quality of the information you are getting. Moreover, get some qualitative measure of performance for those managers whose jobs are not quantitative in nature (e.g., morale, advertising, labor relations, etc.)

Cut the paperwork associated with controls. A system will break down fast when reports become the *end* instead of the *means.*

Chapter 13

BOARD OF DIRECTORS: RUBBER STAMPS?

"The Board: It's obsolete unless overhauled"
—*Business Week*

In the past year or so we have witnessed a growing number of failures, near failures, and sorry operating records by American corporations. During the inevitable autopsy that has followed, dozens of managerial pathologists have speculated about the causes of these slides.

The causes are complex and diverse. However, there is unanimous agreement that much of the fault lies at the door of a traditional American business institution—*The Board of Directors.*

The problem

Although it is not exactly clear what the involved boards could have done to prevent the profit slides, it is abundantly clear that in the majority of cases they failed to keep their fingers on the pulse of the companies they were supposed to guide. This situation has led, in turn, to an examination of the institution of the board itself—its functions, responsibilities, composition and organization.

The problem was recently succinctly stated by *Business Week:*

"There was a time when a corporate director could regard his appointment as just an agreeable tribute to his wealth and his connections, a sign that he had entered the inner circle of the business community. If any director still thinks of his job that way, the proliferation of stockholder suits, the drumfire criticism of the militant consumerists, and the mounting complaints of minority groups should make him think again.

"The problem of the modern director is to define his role so that he does not meddle with day-to-day management but nevertheless knows what is going on and makes his influence felt in the determination of broad policy. It is not a problem that lends itself to easy answers. Each company is a separate case, and it is fair to ask whether a man who serves on a dozen or more boards really is doing his job on any of them.

"In too many recent cases—Penn Central, for example—no one has been more surprised than the directors when the management finally admitted that the company was in deep trouble. And in too many cases, consumer groups or spokesmen for minorities have hit home when they charged that no one on the corporate board was thinking about them. As a result, business today is more vulnerable to punitive legislation and regulation than it has been at any time since the 1930's.

"If corporate management is to survive in anything like its present form, directors will have to take on new responsibilities. They must make sure that corporate goals are consistent with the larger goals of U.S. society. And they must monitor management to see that it pursues these goals effectively, including the basic objective of earning a reasonable income and keeping the company out of the bankruptcy courts."

Precedents: Penn Central, LTV, et al.

There are an abundance of examples of how corporate boards failed in their jobs—Texas Gulf Sulphur, Chrysler, etc.—but for purposes of illustration, examine two more.

Penn Central financial data was fabricated and distorted to an unbelievable extent. Yet neither directors nor banking groups picked it up in time. Sixteen underwriters at Lloyds of London filed a joint suit to cancel liability insurance policies that protected directors of Penn Central. The board members were uninformed and unquestioning, and failed in their basic and primary responsibility as *trustees* for the shareholders.

James J. Ling was steering LTV toward the brink of disaster for a long time without any questions from his board. The purchase of

81 percent interest in Jones & Laughlin Steel Corp., with a tender offer of $85 per share against $50 market price, "sailed through" without debate. Ling could "do no wrong," thought the board. Two years later the same directors removed Ling from active management, but only after a series of disasters. Growing ailments of J. & L., Justice Department anti-trust action, mounting debt and interest expenses, melting profits and pressure amounting to an "ultimatum" from LTV debt holders, finally *persuaded* the board to make a move.

Why the problem?

The reasons for the ineffectiveness of boards are complex, but a number of obvious ones emerge. Look at a few:

The director's job is no longer a prestige sinecure

What was an occasional prestige job of attending monthly or quarterly meetings and getting a free meal at an exclusive business luncheon club is now a demanding and nerve-racking responsibility.

The pressure from government, regulatory agencies, minority and civic groups, proxy fights, auditors, militant students and the public in general, has made a directorship hard work with little reward.

Many members of boards wish they had never accepted the positions, and companies have problems finding replacements.

Lethargic board members

The key reason for lethargic boards is the false sense of security of the outside directors who remember the quiet "good old days." They do not question, they do not inquire, they do not press for information. They do not "make waves," says Keith Louden, an expert on the subject.

Often they are personal friends of the chief executive and other operating executives. They trust his judgment and relinquish their trusteeship role.

Stockholders' suits are growing like poison ivy

Minority shareholders are suing companies for various reasons. In Los Angeles, the payment of $170 million in dividends is challenged as it came out of the surplus of a recently acquired company. In Texas, a $137 million suit charges an insurance company with making illegal loans to gambling interests. Other suits involve conflicts of interest, incorrect registration statements, "insiders' " profits, withholding information from stockholders, and so on.

Liability insurance for directors is expensive. Only a handful of insurers will write it, and they do not protect the directors when negligence and fraud are proven in court.

The outsider member is an expert—that's a laugh

Chrysler's board became mesmerized by Townsend and abdicated the duty of examining cost and financial controls despite financial expertise of the board. The directors of General Dynamics and AT&T did not perform much better. Frequently bankers and lawyers are a liability, not an asset to a company board. They gradually change their point of view from one of professional and objective expertise to an emotional and irrational loyalty to the company, and blindly approve actions they would unmercifully question in their own offices.

Dominance of the board by the insiders

An insider majority destroys the entire purpose—the trusteeship function of the board. The operating management becomes the judge, the jury and the prosecuting attorney; the shareholder has no chance, except not to invest in the first place or sell fast.

A majority of outsiders does not mean that the trusteeship function is fulfilled. The insiders all vote and support the chief executive officer—after all, he can fire them if they don't. They cannot be independent and truthful; they only fill out board seats. If the outsiders are apathetic, don't ask questions, don't discuss and "rubber stamp" insiders' propositions, the board becomes a very weak and ineffective instrument of audit and control. Such a board (and this is a common prototype of large corporation boards) is a dangerous phenomenon. *No* board would be better— stockholders would pay more attention instead of being deceived that someone intelligent and dedicated is looking after their interests.

Overhaul the board: duties and responsibilities

What are the functions of a board of directors suited to today's conditions? Keith Louden gives a good definition in his book, *The Corporate Director:*

> "The board of directors is, by law, accountable to the owners for prudent, effective employment of the owners' investment in the business.
> "The board meets this obligation by:
> 1. Appointing a competent chief executive officer
> 2. Delegating to him wide latitude and authority for managing the company's affairs
> 3. Keeping informed on the company's performance
> 4. Retaining the right to take action in the event of a serious departure from prudent, effective employment of the owners' investment."

The above means, in plain language:

(1) The chief executive officer is hired by and reports to the board. If he doesn't perform, he can and should be fired by the board. Too many boards are dominated by the chief executive officer. The members forget that *they* are the bosses.

(2) Delegation does not mean abdication. The board should examine and approve major strategies and policies, and delegate the implementation to the operating people. It must check and audit whether the strategies are working and if the performance matches the plans and commitments.

(3) The board must request latest and timely financial and operating information; study it, check it, audit it. The board members must feel the pulse of the corporation and know at all times the state of health of their "ward."

(4) The directors must take immediate and relevant action whenever there is a beginning of downturn or any upset in operations. They should not expect the chief executive to do the right thing at all times. They basically should *not* trust him, but audit and control him.

Overhaul the board: hire directors carefully

They are ultimately responsible for the success or the failure of the company. The selection of board members is of utmost importance to the well-being and the survival of the corporation.

(a) They should be experts in their fields—marketing, engineering, finance, production, foreign trade. These fields should be relevant to the company's business.

(b) They should be sound, proven, experienced businessmen.

(c) They should not be symbolic minority representatives, selected for "show" by public relations hucksters. The appointment of a black woman diplomat to the board of IBM fits into that category, but the "multiple use" aspect of the selection shows at least imagination.

(d) They should not be lawyers, bankers or consultants with whom the company deals. This could create potential conflicts of interest, and they do not contribute any more as directors than as members of their respective firms providing paid services.

(e) They should not be selected because of prestige, patronage, reciprocity, friendship, pressures, personal obligation or any other reason than business competence relevant to the corporate operations.

(f) They should be paid handsomely for their services, not a token $3,000, $5,000 or even $10,000 yearly retainer, but a sum sufficient to reimburse them for their expertise, their time and their "homework"—preparation, study and analysis of data for each meeting. If they don't have time to thoroughly prepare themselves, don't bring them aboard— under any circumstances.

(g) They must have a true conviction that they are *trustees* for the owners and the dedication to *act* in that fashion.

When the spineless "rubber stamp" uninformed director is replaced by a live stimulator, catalyst, questioner and needler, we will achieve better corporate results and better protection for the stockholders.

LESSONS TO BE LEARNED

(1) The Board of Directors must become an active and dynamic top decision-making, top decision-approving, and top decision-reviewing body.

(2) The days of the "rubber stamp," "cosmetic," prestige director are gone.

(3) A fully functioning director must devote enough time to fully understand the company's operations and problems. He must be well compensated and should not have any direct or indirect conflicts of interest.

(4) A "new breed" director should represent all stockholders, not just special interests. *Token* minority representatives, elected for public relations reasons, should also be avoided.

(5) All inside directors—puppet directors—should be eliminated, except the chief executive officer. They should be replaced by outside directors who are independent of the CEO. That means no relatives, country club friends, other CEO's, bankers, lawyers, or personal consultants.

(6) New laws and vigorous enforcement of existing statutes will make a director's job far more difficult and dangerous than in the past. Liability suits for large amounts are a reality, not just a remote potential threat.

(7) There is an increasing need and demand for professional directors.

(8) The *new* Board of Directors must be the boss and the judge of the chief executive officer, not vice versa. This is a hard recipe for most CEO's to accept and follow.

Chapter 14

ONE-MAN RULE: THE SHADOW OF THE LEADER IS SHORTENING FAST

"An institution is the lengthened shadow
of one man."
                    —Emerson (1841)

Emerson's famous quotation has been true for more than a century—and still is. However, like all quotations and cliches of the past, it must be constantly modified and updated.

The history of American business is studded with successful one-man rules. The rise of many of today's largest corporations is due for the most part to the individual genius and personality of a determined entrepreneur. The Mellons, the Carnegies or the Rockefellers, robber barons of the turn of the century, were extraordinarily successful without practicing consultative or participative management. The curbing of the excesses and iniquities of these entrepreneurs through legislation—Supreme Court decisions and the anti-trust laws—did not modify the fact that during the first half of this century spectacular business success was the result of a one-man show.

The classical, autocratic, baronial patriarch of the past is not good enough for today's complexities. Let's look at some of the "Caesars" of the recent past who held out too long.

Recent one man shows

RCA was the "baby" of David Sarnoff, whose technological

dreams and visions came true despite the expert opinions of cynics and skeptics to the contrary. The "General" and RCA were synonymous. But while his insistence on producing color television in the fifties and sixties proved correct and ultimately profitable, the twenty years of RCA ventures into computers turned from bad to worse, and the seventies witnessed the admittance of failure in that field. RCA divestiture of all computer operations will require a write-off of some $500 million when all the costs are added up.

The entire *airline industry,* recently in deep troubles, was the product of rugged individualists and entrepreneurs. C.R. Smith ruled American Airlines for some thirty years and made it tick. Juan Trippe stayed almost as long with Pan Am, making it *the* international airline. "Captain" Eddie Rickenbacker made Eastern, and "Pat" Patterson made United. Even the smaller National Airlines had the indelible imprint of its founder and air-pioneer, L.B. Maytag.

But, again in the late sixties and seventies, changing priorities changed the fortunes of the airlines. The old pilots had the ability to fly and manage by the seats of their pants. But the sixties brought new complexities, new problems and a demand for more precise management. The mistakes with jumbo jets, lack of planning for physical handling facilities, gradual neglect of customer service, employee rudeness and inefficiency, all combined to demand new managements and new techniques.

While the five-year annual sales growth of the twelve major U.S. airlines averaged 11.8 percent, the annual earnings per share growth was negative for all of them. Six declined over the five years from 3.2 percent to 31 percent, and six went into a deficit position.

The growth of DuPont into a world industrial power must be attributed to the succession of the DuPont "Caesars." After General Henry DuPont's one-man control for almost forty years, a true dynasty was formed: Coleman DuPont, Irenee DuPont, and Lamont DuPont continued the family rule and succeeded in making DuPont a paragon of the world's chemical industry and a leader in innovation, research and production.

While all the textbooks give DuPont a grade "A+" for their profit planning system and their methods of financial control, the company has been fumbling in an organizational quandry since the late sixties. This is ironical, since it was voted by a panel of 300 corporation presidents as one of the ten best-managed companies in the U.S., with special emphasis on "financial acumen." The five-year cumulative sales growth of DuPont was 3.8 percent, but the earnings per share actually declined by 3.4 percent. Their stock is at the same level as five years ago. One must admit that the entire chemical industry had indigestion from overcapacity during the same period, but one would have expected a better performance from the undisputed leader of some seventy years. The company's troubles can be traced to a holdover managerial philosophy of centralization.

Ernest Dale, in his book, *The Great Organizers,* calls Ernest Tenner Weir of National Steel the "Iconoclast of Management." Weir started with a small tin plate mill and expanded it to become a large and profitable integrated steel producer. His tenure of some twenty-seven years as chief executive was turbulent, but all the decisions and plans were his and his alone. His control of costs was spectacular: at one time during the Great Depression, National Steel made a profit while every other steel company—including the giant U.S. Steel—was suffering a loss. At one time, it is said, U.S. Steel tried to buy Weir by offering him the presidency at an annual salary of $1 million. Weir refused—he liked to run his own show.

Operating results of the past five years (1966-72) were dull and far from any semblance of the successful past. While the cumulative sales increased by 6.7 percent, the five-year annual earnings-per-share growth was -10.7 percent. The stock was some 3 percent below the five-year-ago level.

Paul Galvin of Motorola, Colonel Rockwell of Rockwell Manufacturing Company, Armand Hammer of Occidental Petroleum, Joe Wilson of Xerox, "Gussie" Busch, Jr. of Budweiser, Henry Kaiser of Kaiser Industries, Paul Getty, and, of course, Howard Hughes—the list is endless. All of these men provided the key ingredient to the emergence and growth of a successful corporation in the first fifty years of this century. To a large extent, the secret was the "lengthened shadow of one man." One-man rule and one-man control was good. However, by holding on too long into the sixties and seventies, the classical manager of the past couldn't cope with the complexities of the present.

Three classical autocrats

Both the good—and the bad—of one-man rule can be judged against the historical and current backdrop of three classical cases.

The Henry Ford rule

Henry Ford is an extreme but excellent classroom example of how times changed while the man did not. Ford's genius was in his understanding of machines. His shortcoming was his ignorance of men. He was the first to grasp the potential of technology and apply it to mass-production techniques, which revolutionized our industrial world. His assembly line dehumanized workers, but opened up huge markets by producing cars at low prices.

Ford once remarked, "The average man won't easily do a day's work unless he is caught and can't get out of it." He kept tabs on workers and everything else in the company through a superbly organized system of spies and informers. His workers were instantly fired for smoking; talking on the job was forbidden; employees were not allowed to go to the toilet unless a substitute was available. His philosophy of operations was simple: keep the *machinery* rolling—if it needs people, buy them with high wages, company stores, full employment guarantee, and keep them in constant fear of losing their jobs to prevent any complaints.

Ford is still a hero and a legend; his errors were monumental. He resisted innovation, banned advertising, vetoed mechanical improvements, and ignored cost reports and balance sheets. When the family forced his retirement in 1945, the company teetered on the brink of bankruptcy.

The T.J. Watson, Sr. rule

Thomas Watson of IBM was far more a benevolent dictator than Henry Ford, but he, too, ruled with an iron fist. Employees had to abide by strict regulations on dress (white shirts and hats) and personal habits (no smoking or drinking). At one time IBM had no female secretaries. But Watson was also paternalistic to the extreme: employees were all part of the IBM family, they sang songs together, went to the IBM recreation grounds together, they lived and breathed IBM during and off their working hours. Management by fear was the accepted control tool, and apparently an acceptable one. A high executive of the company was once unexpectedly summoned from a business trip in Kansas to the World Headquarters in New York and was made to wait for three full days in front of Watson, Sr.'s office. By the end of that time, he was a nervous wreck and sure that he was going to be fired or demoted. The "boss" finally saw him and announced his promotion to vice-president. The reason for this rather cruel mental torture—"Keep them off balance! It will make them work harder."

The timely succession of T.J. Watson, Jr., who had the same characteristics as his father but to a lesser degree, and who was more adapted to the modern world, avoided the Ford-type downturn by IBM.

T. Vincent Learson, the recently appointed chairman, is said to believe in his predecessor's managerial philosophy and things are "tougher than ever" at IBM. Frank Cary, the successor to Learson's rule, has a distinctly different style of management. A new IBM era may begin.

Conglomeration and one-man rule

During the past ten years, we have witnessed a new phenomenon: the emergence and the rapid growth of conglomerates. While the Caesars of the past took twenty and even forty years to grow their companies from within, the new breed of entrepreneurs, the go-go conglomerators, took the outside route of mergers, acquisitions and high-multiple leverage—the "funny money" route. And here again the spectacular growth and initial success of many conglomerates was due to the one-man rule—the fast and unopposed decisions of the "boss"—in many cases a truly charismatic personality.

H.E. Figge was the wonder boy of Automatic Sprinkler (now A.T.O.); Jim Ling could do no wrong at LTV. Bernie Cornfeld became Europe's instant king of cash and created in a few years the world's largest financial institution. A less well-known William

M. Duke took charge at Whittaker and in five years lifted its sales from \$43 to \$793 million. Charles Bluhdorn, of Gulf & Western, had innumerable articles written on his perspicacity and fast decision-making ability. All of these men had their imitators, and suddenly some of America's greatest companies began acquiring or being acquired.

The collapse of conglomerates was swift and dramatic, and the entrepreneurial go-go boys were unable to *manage* the unstable empires they created through a combination of a numbers game, permissive accounting, stock market fervor and a very short-term strategy. The modern industrial Caesars enjoyed a far shorter reign (five years) than their predecessors (20-40 years).

Why did the conglomerates fail? Although the basic reasons were covered in Chapter 7, the fundamental problem was one of one-man rule. The operating companies described above failed because of the changes in the "human equation," marketing shifts, and technological developments. These "oldtimers" were unable or refused to accommodate to these changes. But they went down swinging—*managing* their companies and attempting to get better sales, improved production, and financial success based on operations. The "financial wizards" were interested more in financial dealing than in making a profit through operations. Their "jazz up the stock" syndrome was another form of one-man rule.

Break down of the dynasty system

The pivotal characteristic of the long-term one-man ruler of the past was his absence of attention to the human element. He believed that people accepted and executed orders, appreciated paternalism, and tolerated abusive and unfair treatment. Jobs were scarce, and the employer's attitude was not much different anyplace else. Thus, while technologies and material factors changed, the employee attitude, or his resignation to the status quo, was static—the resentment may have been increasing, but it was suppressed or sublimated and did not reflect itself in any concrete counter-action.

Under the circumstances, the business despot did not have to concern himself with "people's problems" in order to set examples. He needed to understand better than anybody else the production and assembly side of the business; the production of goods and services at a competitive price through increasing use of automation and capital equipment. Even the marketing element was far less "human" than today. The consumer had less discretionary income, less selectivity and less education—he was price (rather than style or quality) conscious, and he was more gullible.

The change of the human equation

Perhaps the key reason for the downfall of the long-term rulers and for the decline of the companies they ruled is the accelerating change in the so called "human equation." Behavioral scientists (e. g., Likert, McGregor, Herzberg) have advanced theories about change of attitudes, different priorities of motives, the importance of self-respect, the need for self-actualization, and the need for recognition. Over a period of fifteen or more years their theories were widely discussed and agreed with. Managers were sent to seminars, to executive development sessions, or back to graduate school for college refresher courses. But staid managements of successful companies continued to pay lip service to the new "theories" of human relations and pursued their "proven" policies of management by fear and by edict. There was some artificial and superficial pretense of cross-communication, listening to the grass roots and participative and consultative management, but it was mostly window dressing.

The situation began to change rapidly when the American employee began to assert his independence, prompted probably quite unconsciously by the many social movements of self-determination: the unions, the college students, the women's liberation movement, the changes in sexual and moral codes and practices, and the self-assertion of minorities. The new business manager did not want to be a pawn any more—he wanted to be heard, and if he could not get his day in the sun, he quit. Talented men are obviously essential to the success of any enterprise, and one-man-rule companies began to lose talent. Some went to create their own companies, some joined competitors, and others preferred smaller, more "personal" corporations.

The long-term one-man rule depended on a "dehumanized" policy of management. Such a policy is no longer valid today.

Technological and social changes

The increasing rate of change has added orders of magnitude to the complexity of running an organization. Two main factors contribute to this phenomenon simultaneously:

A. *Consumerism:* The consumer is becoming more demanding and selective. The proven past formulas for marketing are ineffective and must be changed. Lotz, president of Volkswagen, found this out when the Japanese Toyotas and Datsuns began to outsell the "bug." When profits dipped, Lotz was fired.

Zanuck, the king of Twentieth Century Fox, left the scene after the company lost hundreds of millions of dollars producing films which the public did not wish to see.

The staid, imperturbable A&P ran into marketing troubles when its policies did not change with the times. Profits plummeted and a major management purge was undertaken, the first time in decades of "orderly" progress.

B. *Technology:* The effects of billions of dollars of R&D are spreading across all industries. Obsolescence of any product or service is accelerating to a degree unthinkable a few years ago. The electronics industry is fighting the battle of the components—computers are obsolete by the time the production lines are set and the specifications frozen. New plastics and chemical compounds are introduced daily on the industrial scene, making supply decisions extremely complex. Improvements or innovations in machinery and automated production systems make capital investments obsolete long before the expected amortization timetable.

Thus the long-term Caesar must adapt himself to the new conditions, but his past experience is more of a detriment than a help. He begins to lack the feel of the market and the technical knowledge. He cannot bluff his way out, since he has no team of talented people to rely on, and his "troops" begin to "rebel." And so the company begins to slip, not slowly but rapidly, and often reaches the point of no return.

LESSONS TO BE LEARNED

What are then the alternatives? How should a chief executive manage in this brave new world of today—a world not only different from yesterday, but rapidly and constantly changing?

The students of management, the new breed of professors, authors, and consultants from top business schools of the country, have written innumerable words on the new practice of management. They usually agree on the following points:

(1) The one-man rule should be eliminated.

(2) Management should be participative and consultative.

(3) Each executive should have his responsibilities well defined.

(4) Authority and responsibility should be delegated.

(5) Managers should be encouraged to use their judgment and initiative.

(6) Good communications should be established downwards, upwards, laterally and across.

(7) Each man should understand what is expected from him and commit himself to the fulfillment of the objectives.

(8) Personnel should be motivated to action by monetary and non-monetary incentives—there should be an atmosphere of enthusiasm, not of fear.

(9) Free expression and interchange of ideas and views should be encouraged.

(10) Plans and decisions should be discussed among many. Dissent and minority opinions should be encouraged to examine all facets of a problem.

(11) Decentralization into small profit centers is desirable to keep the "small company entrepreneurial spirit" alive and burning.

(12) Short, intermediate and long-range planning throughout the organization should be instituted and given top priority.

(13) Innovation, new ideas, and a go-go spirit should be stimulated throughout the organization.

Chapter 15

SLOW REACTION TO CHANGE: YOU CAN'T PLAN THE FUTURE ON THE PAST

> "I want to study change in order to gain power over it."
>
> —McLuhan

A feature story in *The Wall Street Journal* commented:

> Businessmen, and their critics alike, agree that the concept of growth and profit as measured by traditional balance sheets and profit-and-loss statements are too narrow to reflect what many modern corporations are trying to do.

A great number of old pioneers (e. g., Carnegie, Ford, Rockefeller, Vanderbilt) would turn over in their graves if they heard this statement. Isn't profit the name of the game? The answer is: Yes and No! We must have profit for corporate longevity, but both profits and longevity are being increasingly influenced by the way the manager and his organization react to change, both in the marketplace and as a corporate citizen.

Those top executives that react slowly to change—and most do—are suddenly meeting a whole array of social issues in addition to the normally complex market changes. Social issues include pollution, racial discrimination, consumerism, and similar problems that seriously and directly affect their corporate operations.

For the most part, issues don't get dealt with until they become issues. So many managers are asking the questions: Why didn't we do something about this issue before it happened? What could we have done? What do we do in the future?

Until recently, there was no public outcry against dumping pollutants into rivers or refusing to hire uneducated blacks. Therefore, businessmen did not have to speak 'the language of "social responsibility." Until recently, businessmen didn't have to concern themselves too much with accelerating market changes such as the proliferation of products, consumerism, "marketing myopia," and such.

All this has changed. The businessman must now plan for change and react *before* specific change becomes an issue.

Social change: a business dilemma

Until around 1968-69, social responsibility was a concept that General Motors had yet to develop. Top management seemed unaware of the emerging public consensus that it should meet higher standards of quality and safety. The idea was beginning to spread that businessmen must assume new responsibilities (and *costs*) for the benefit of the public. Moreover, they should do this even in the face of reduced profits.

Ralph Nader's attacks came as almost paralyzing shocks to G.M.'s executives. Following intuition rather than theory, Nader had become an *ex officio* national figure whom politicians and businessmen have had to reckon with ever since. He single-handedly brought down the market for G.M.'s Corvair. The initial response of many of the company's executives was to lash out and assail the critic, using as their crutch such outworn clichés as "free enterprise," "What's good for G.M.," and "business prerogatives." The 1970 annual meeting was a special jolt. A Nader-affiliated group, the *Campaign to Make General Motors Responsible,* proposed that G.M. elect three directors representing the public and create a stockholder committee on corporate responsibility. These demands were a real shocker. Nevertheless, G.M. did establish a Public Policy Committee of the board and elected the Reverend Leon Sullivan, a black man, as a member of the board.

G.M. is now socially responsible; indeed, the company feels it has no choice about the matter. And the cost is high. In 1971 alone, the company spent more than $200 million on pollution controls and $400 million on safety research, plus additional millions on research in new transportation methods. It is becoming increasingly clear that the cost of the company's "social" efforts will make a permanent erosion in its normal level of profits and return on investment.

The chairman of General Motors has long been viewed as having the biggest job in U.S. business. It is interesting to note that the 1972 chairman, Richard Gerstenberg, views his job in terms of full-time concern with *change*—not the conventional functions of operation, marketing, or finance.

The venerable Great Atlantic & Pacific Tea Company gets into serious trouble with their "up the blacks" attitude. Union Carbide earns a place on the cover of a national magazine as "America's most polluted company." There is hardly a major company that has not been touched in some way by the new demand that they be socially responsible.

The dilemma

A lot of businessmen, are asking the justifiable question: What does the public want—what else can business do?

In the last twenty years business has made enormous strides and the general population has benefited greatly. The flow of goods and services has more than doubled. Despite the fears that automation would reduce employment, the number of people employed has increased much faster than the adult population. The quality of work has been upgraded by reducing the back-breaking toil and repetitive, mind-numbing tasks. While semi-skilled workers increased only 15 percent, professional and technical workers increased 148 percent and clerical workers 80 percent. The fruits of this economic upsurge, whether in the dignity of the work itself or in the products of the work, are more widely and less inequitably distributed than they used to be. Popular participation in the ownership of industry, both directly and through pension funds, has vastly increased. Insecurity, brought on by periodic business cycles, has decreased. Why does the public flail the "business establishment"?

Despite these advances that have been achieved by the economic system, business is continually being denounced for those very achievements. The man who hates his work blames business. People who convince themselves that they are working only for material rewards tell themselves that these rewards are morally corrupting. Only 50 members of a graduating class at Harvard said they wanted to enter business. People accuse business of corrupting the society's soul by pampering its body. Yet, as people's expectations rise faster than their buying power, business is blamed for the resulting discontent. It appears that the unhappiness of the population is projected upon the economic system as the well of social "sickness."

It is as though the nation had "corporate hypochondria." Popular books such as *The Greening of America, The Sick Society, America Inc.,* flail The Establishment, whatever that is. The problem for most businessmen is that those who are suffering from "corporate hypochondria" see the institution of business as the establishment.

Yet, the businessman must be socially responsible.

Social responsibility makes good sense

Ralph Nader is not the only guardian of the public good. Churches, educational institutions, mutual funds, publishers, voluntary organizations, and businessmen themselves are among those vocal and dedicated groups who are concentrating on issues that are in the vanguard of the corporate responsibility movement: urban affairs, environment, consumerism, corporate reform, and legal challenges from public-interest activists.

The United Church of Christ has worked up a 61-page booklet on "Investing Funds for Maximum Social Impact." The Dreyfus Third Century Fund leads the growing number of investment organizations dedicated to investing in firms that "improve the quality of life in the United States." A prestigious quarterly, *Business & Society Review,* is published for those "concerned businessmen" who are seeking social change via the free enterprise system. These and many other examples go to show how the advancing cause of social responsibility cannot be sidestepped. It is now a way of corporate life.

For the most part, the modern executive admits his responsibility and the responsibility of his company to society. The classical concept of profit only is no longer good. New customs, new ways of doing business have replaced the old. Consider these comments by chief executives of some of the country's biggest companies.

> There are things you know you should do about unemployment and other social considerations which from a strict monetary approach would not appear to be a good decision.
>
> One of the greatest responsibilities of the corporate executive is to ensure the climate that makes it possible to grow in the future, and that means the whole environment.
>
> Society is the platform from which we work.
>
> If we do not solve social problems, the economy will go to hell and we with it.

Market planning

If one were to examine a list of twenty-five industrial corporations with the largest assets in 1929 and examine this same list now, a number of companies would be missing. Ten of these 1929 companies, with their 1970 ranking are: Anaconda (45), Armour (150), International Harvester (37), Uniroyal (79), Swift (128), Kennecott Copper (52), Republic Steel (44), Pullman (198), Sinclair (merged with Atlantic Richfield), and General Theatres Equipment (bankrupt). They have been replaced at the top by IBM, General Telephone, ITT, Chrysler, Atlantic Richfield, Tenneco, Phillips Petroleum, Continental Oil, and Eastman Kodak.

This changing mix of successful and not-so-successful companies tends to prove two things: first, that changing markets and products provide opportunities for those companies that can take advantage of them. Second, those firms that fail to keep up-to-date on market changes can fall behind. The conclusion emerges that today's executive should keep abreast of market changes and react to them.

Consider the case of Chrysler, that on-again off-again automaker. Its chairman, Lynn Townsend, had extraordinary powers to run the company, and he did make substantial improvements until changes in the market appeared—changes to which Chrysler did not react in time. First, the company maintained a high production rate of 1971 model big cars despite the obvious fact that the big car was not selling. They failed to identify and react

to a market change toward the small and intermediate-size automobile. Second, the company completely missed the boat when
the small car (eg., Pinto, Vega) fad swept the country. Being
unprepared, they were forced into the importation of an inferior
foreign substitute. Third, the company trailed the competition in
the entry into foreign markets. By reacting too late, Chrysler had
to settle for acquisition of the less attractive companies and had to
spend $500 million and send planeloads of Detroit executives in
an attempt to reorganize its foreign subsidiaries.

The truly successful corporations discovered early that marketing is the most important function of a business. The spectacular
growth patterns of an IBM, Avon, Xerox, or Sears have been due to
their marketing acumen and their attention, bordering on devo-
tion, to the marketplace. A company may have the greatest
technological know-how, a super-efficient production facility, or
the most astute financial management, but if their marketing
efforts are off target, the company will falter.

Changes in the marketplace

Our economic growth and high standard of living are due in
large degree to our mass-producing and mass-marketing ability for
a huge variety of goods and services. Attention to the marketplace,
respect for the customer demands and elaborate marketing and
selling efforts are not new, but fundamental to the U.S. business
enterprise system. Are there any significant, basic changes occurring in the marketplace to upset or confuse the established
expertise of our successful corporations? The answer is yes; the
changes are not revolutionary in nature, but in *timing*. The general
acceleration of change in all parts of our society generate those in
the marketplace. These are summarized here and discussed below:

(1) The general proliferation of products.
(2) The Systems Approach to marketing.
(3) The changing life cycle of products.
(4) Marketing myopia.

Production proliferation

In what has become the "decade of the consumer," economists
and businessmen in the 1970's aren't taking anything for granted.

The consumer is a different breed of cat. He thinks differently, shops differently, spends differently. He demands, and gets, a much wider variety of choices.

Take the case of the "complex bra." Its evolution is an example of product proliferation. Several years ago ladies' brassieres were mostly made of cotton, were white, functional, and not subject to much discussion or shopping alternatives. The only other color was black and the ratio was about 10 to 1, with white winning. But gradually the utility of undergarments changed to the style of lingerie and underfashions, as women required style in addition to functionality in these items. The "bust cult" demanded innovation in padding to accentuate or improve the natural look. In addition to the improvement of the figure, women demanded color. Thus, like cars, bras began to be manufactured in blue, yellow, black, red, pink, violet, tan, purple, mint, and in floral and multi-color prints. Materials proliferated with the advent of rayon, acetate, nylon and other artificial fibers. The use of mix of materials increased, including the addition of tricot, nets, lace, stretchable fabrics and ornamental trimmings. The demand and the styles began to reflect the increasing complexity of today's world. The number of combinations and permutations of styles, sizes, fabrics and colors zoomed into the thousands, while the *total* demand and the market potential grew at a rate parallel to the growth of the female population. In fact, recent growth has been even slower due to the "no bra" fad among the younger set.

Making very rough comparisons and calculations, we can conservatively say that in twenty years market changes have made bra styling, production, scheduling, and delivery *35* times more complicated. This has been accomplished *without* corresponding advantages in market expansion or profitability. In other words, the company had to be 35 times "smarter" to stay even.

Similar conditions prevail in the marketing of computers, automobiles, garden supplies, packaged breakfast cereals, or almost any product you can name. The generalization that we wish to draw is that the higher standard of living, the higher educational level and the higher overall sophistication of the customer has created a desire for individuality, customization and differentiation that has fragmentalized the mass market. Thus, a business enterprise that has prospered on true mass production—"you can have any color car as long as it's black"—must truly *innovate* on creating "customized" mass production, in order to maintain its cost structure commensurate with the diversified and faster changing customer demands.

System marketing

Another key element of marketing change is the systems concept. A customer does not buy a product; he buys the end use that the product provides. One product may not be sufficient by itself to give complete satisfaction. For instance, the best grass seed does *not* give the customer what he really wants: a beautiful lawn. He needs, in addition to the grass seed, a combination of fertilizers, pesticides, weed killers, as well as spreaders, sprayers and lawn mowers. The customer needs a *system* of lawn maintenance. A company must understand this deceptively simple concept or it will not prosper in the seventies—the age of systems. An industrial customer no longer wants to buy a valve from a good valve producer. He needs a system that provides effective flow and control of liquids through his plant. The valve manufacturer had better be prepared to understand these demands or his valve business will collapse.

Even the computer manufacturers were surprised how fast "software" became dominant and how difficult it is to sell "hardware" alone. Indeed, IBM's lion's share of the market was obtained on this principle.

The system concept will become even more popular as our socio-economic environment will not be able to operate without a complete inter-relationship of presently disconnected parts. What good is a 3000 miles per hour airplane, crossing the Atlantic in two hours, if it takes a passenger 1-1/2 hours to reach the airport, 1/2 hour to find a parking spot, one hour to check in together with his 500 co-passengers, 1/2 hour to board the giant plane and find his seat, and finally wait another 1-1/2 hours for traffic control to allow take-off. If you add the same 4-5 hours on the other end of the journey, you reach the exaggerated situation of a 2-hour flight and a 10-hour or more pre- and post-flight activities. What we really need is a system of transportation and not an uncoordinated piecemeal approach to the problem.

Obviously the concept, the example, and the need are not new. And yet very little *real* progress is being made in the direction of the systems approach. We are usually pushed to action by a crisis. Thus, a badly needed, very expensive air traffic control system will probably be ordered on a crash program basis, only after two supersonic planes, each carrying 400 passengers, collide in mid-air over Washington, D.C. Similarly, business enterprises will fully move ahead with an integrated system approach only after their profits and their markets begin to shrink and decline.

Shorter product life cycles

The third key element of change in the marketplace is a direct by-product of the technological explosion and the "time compression" principle. Products simply don't last as long. This causes problems in manufacturing, as well as marketing. The basic life cycle of new products is the well-known "S" curve. (Figure 15-1)

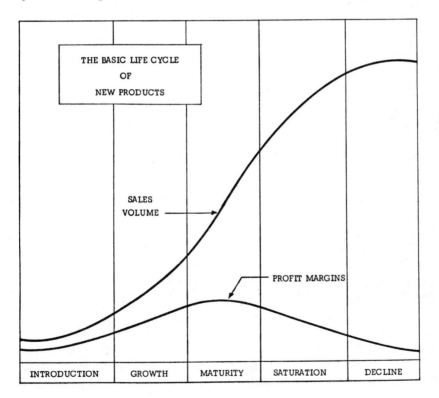

Figure 15-1

Today, however, the slope of the sales volume curve is becoming steeper and steeper. Thus, if a business is not ready to exploit an opportunity in a short time and make this decision faster than ever before, it will be ready too late, and it will find itself faster at the declining phase of profits. It is also well known that profits start declining when the sales curve still climbs. This is due to the many latecomers entering the market and eroding the sales price, trying to buy their entry into the market. Thus begins a costly and unprofitable fight for the share of the market which produces generally no winners and many losers. The food franchise businesses are a good example.

One of the generalizations to be made from the above is: The new conditions favor finding new and virgin markets, effecting a fast super-growth penetration for fast profits, and then abandoning the field to others for the fruitless "share of the market" competition.

The ever-present marketing myopia

The fourth element of change is again not new, but managers have not yet learned their lesson from the past. It is the problem of *marketing myopia.* Harvard's Theodore Levitt described this phenomenon in a brilliant argument in his book, *Innovation in Marketing.* The term was coined in a *Harvard Business Review* article and rapidly became a classic term in business circles. His very correct thesis is that established businesses either do not foresee or choose to disregard clues of major market changes. The result is that other industries, previously strangers to the product field, come in, and cash in.

Levitt's examples are numerous. General Electric turned down the opportunity to get exclusive American rights to manufacture and distribute neon lights, concluding that there was no market for them. Frozen orange juice had to be started by a company not in the food business. The big hotel chains fought the motel idea for years. Major improvements in gasoline quality have tended to originate outside the oil industry. Major innovations in automobile fuel marketing have not been introduced by the big producers. The automobile industry decided that the airplane was not very important and never bothered to produce them. The textile industry was so convinced that natural fibers were superior and impervious to competition, that it took the chemical industry to pioneer and profit by the introduction of artificial fibers. The railroads never thought of being in the transportation business and therefore ignored air and road transportation opportunities. When Carlson offered his basic xerographic patent for sale in 1949, none of the big companies (3M, IBM, NCR, Eastman Kodak, DuPont and others) saw any value or potential market in copying machines. A struggling, small Rochester company named Haloid had the foresight and the risk-taking spirit, and developed into the billion-dollar Xerox Corporation. The giants are still looking for the man who said, "No, it won't work," to Chester Carlson.

A business enterprise must rapidly tune its antennas to the marketplace and its latent demands and act upon them, even if considerable risk is involved. To do otherwise is to lose its previous leadership or share of the market position. One would think that corporation executives could learn a lesson from the past, but somehow they have not.

General Dynamics promoted their ill-fated Convair jet with five abreast seating when the customer—the airlines—wanted six abreast. The result was a $430 million write-off for G.D. and a Boeing jet for the airlines.

Chrysler kept building large cars when the customer wanted a small one, but the Japanese came up with their Datsuns and Toyotas on time.

Movie producers were fighting TV as their No. 1 enemy, before realizing that they had a new gold mine in front of them.

The fashion experts predicted the rapid demise of the miniskirt and the blind allegiance of the American women to the dictates of Paris. In one short year, the fashions were "liberated" and the Paris fashion giants were dethroned.

The established manufacturers of wooden yachts did not see the impact of fiberglass on their business. Newcomers unhampered by tradition took over the leadership of the industry as well as the profits.

Mighty Pan-Am, the giant of trans-continental airline operations, was clobbered by a weak competitor (Trans-Caribbean Airways) because they didn't understand the regional differences between the New York-Puerto Rico run as compared to the New York-Paris operation.

LESSONS TO BE LEARNED
WHAT THE EXECUTIVE
AND HIS COMPANY CAN DO ABOUT CHANGE

A number of things can be done to anticipate and react to change—both social change and changes in the marketplace.

Establish social involvement and responsibility as a part of corporate policy and strategy. It isn't enough to pay lip service to social considerations or simply to react on a crash basis when an issue arises.

Organize for change. Assign to a senior vice-president, a board committee, or other organizational entity the responsibility of external awareness and corporate change to accommodate those outside and inside the firm.

Set goals. These will probably be qualitative—quantitative goals concerning social responsibility are difficult. Provide for a periodic audit to determine whether goals are being achieved.

Give marketing the top priority in your organization and let everybody know it. Don't let departments become monuments to themselves and don't let them stress their efficiency to the point of hurting the number one purpose of the business: selling the customer at a profit and keeping him as a customer.

Analyze the changing market and the fluid customer demand. Don't trust your experience or your intuition. The customer is not the same as he was ten years ago, five years ago, or even last year. Scan the marketplace more frequently than you have ever done. Watch for clues or changes—by the time you have all the facts, it may be too late. Don't try to fool the customer—he's getting too smart and the regulatory bodies more powerful.

Don't fragment your market potential into too many pieces. The production distribution and/or inventory costs will kill you. Select the part of the market you can penetrate and plunge into it, fast and hard. Use a rifle, not a shotgun approach. Don't scatter your resources.

Adopt wholeheartedly the system approach. Don't sell the steak or the sizzle, but the steak *and* the sizzle. Don't think of the product, but of the *service* the product provides and the service the customer desires.

Time compression can only be coped with by faster decisions. You must market a new product or service twice as fast and twice as well as you did five years ago. You must abandon an existing product or service twice as fast as you would have considered doing it five years ago, or you will have an obsolete lemon on your hands.

Look at the scene around you and exploit opportunities. Don't protect the past—it will kill you: make your own products and services obsolete. It's better to do it yourself than to have the competition do it for you. Look broadly at the whole world—it's small and shrinking—and then pinpoint the piece of the market that is *there* and no one is doing anything about yet.

Chapter 16

CONSUMERISM:
THE CUSTOMER IS KING

"There's a sucker born every minute."
—Phineas Taylor Barnum

The simple fact of life is that Barnum's earthy saying is rapidly becoming obsolete. The American consumer is awakening; he or she is better educated and shrewder than the consumers of just five or ten years ago.

F. Ritter Shumway, Chairman of the Board of the U.S. Chamber of Commerce, believes that the businessman who ignores consumerism, or even takes it lightly, does so at peril to his economic survival.

> "Consumerism is a phenomenon of the great social forces which have revolutionized our age. In fact, it's a product of our increased sophistication: in services, marketing techniques, and in the consumers themselves."
>
> (Chicago Marine Trades Conference, Sept. 1971)

Congress has already passed 26 major consumer protection laws in six years, and this is only the beginning of a major trend. Ralph Nader has had an immense impact on the American public, but he and his "raiders" did not create "consumerism": consumerism created a Ralph Nader. The public resents being treated like a bunch of suckers and is fighting back.

Discretionary income

Once upon a time most economists and marketing men thought that the more the consumer earned, the more he spent. But by the end of the sixties, something went very wrong with this long-accepted theory. In 1968 the government raised taxes, which lowered income, but the consumer went on spending as much as before. In 1970 the government lowered taxes. This meant more money to spend. But the consumer kept it. Instead of buying goods and services, he started hoarding.

George Katona of the University of Michigan is the dean of consumer researchers. In his book, *Aspirations and Affluence,* he and his two associates, Strumpel and Zahn, examine the new "consumer model." Their conclusions are logical: as the consumer grows more affluent and accumulates more "discretionary" income, he begins to wield great economic power. He can spend his money in accordance with his own wishes, his own attitudes and his own judgment. As a great deal of his spending is not for immediate subsistence, he can wait, choose, and drive forecasters and marketeers out of their minds.

Statistics support the above. In 1955, consumers' discretionary income, defined roughly as anything over $10,000 in today's buying power, came to 8 percent of his total personal income. In 1970 it was 20 percent, and will be 30 percent by 1980.

Lack of service

There is a rapid and disturbing decline in the quality of service that the consumer receives while paying more and more for it. The business claim high costs, lack of trained personnel, and growing complexity of the society in general as some of the justifications for the generally accepted problem. Unless companies take really innovative steps to change the situation, the results will be very painful as their sales decline and their profits disappear.

There are examples of deteriorating service and consumer reaction across all segments of our economic endeavors.

Cars

A wealthy executive's wife drives a four year old, dented and rusting station wagon with more than 60,000 miles on the odometer. The plastic imitation paneling has discolored on both sides, and the husband winces every time his shiny, rented limousine leaves him at his driveway near "Mummy's crate," as the children call it. The family could certainly afford to buy a new car. They used to trade both family cars in, every two years, for the past 17 years. The wife decided, however, that she is going to keep her crate until it falls apart or rusts away. "It's really so much less trouble than to go through all the headaches connected with purchasing and "debugging" a new car. And the neighbors don't think we are going broke. A car is no longer a symbol of anything—just transportation."

Automobile manufacturers will have to take a long and hard look at the new attitudes of the buying public to avoid costly mistakes. The impact of the imports, the compact and the sub-compact, the safety regulations, the pollution control, the costs of buying, financing and operating a car—all these and other factors may well be the determinants of not just profitability but actual survival of our large auto makers.

Appliances

A Maytag automatic washer is a dependable product. Its electric motor has even an "overload" protection gadget which acts as a fuse in case of overheating and prevents damage to the expensive motor. When a Maytag washer gave out one morning, the husband, who thought he was mechanically inclined, examined the motor before calling the serviceman. All that was needed was a 59-cent overload protection gizmo that burned out. The Maytag dealer was not interested in replacing a 59-cent part: "We always replace the whole motor for $49, and that's below list price." The husband decided to take matters into his own hands. A closer examination of the motor indicated that it was supplied by General Electric. An attempt was made to buy the small item from the GE Supply Company. The answer was negative: "We don't stock parts made by GE for other manufacturers. We can't even identify the part number, as "contract" parts have different codes, and we are not provided with equivalency charts." By then the washing machine owner was getting impatient and decided to pursue the matter to a final conclusion. He phoned the Maytag headquarters and the General Electric headquarters without great success. The operators kept switching him from one department to another. Finally, he threatened an investigation of collusion and price gouging. A few days later he received the small part in the mail. Although he had to pay for several long distance telephone calls, the net expense was far less than the replacement of the entire motor.

It is difficult to find whether the attempts to charge customers for replacement of entire units rather than repairing them are a corporate policy, a marketing policy or a tolerated custom on the part of the parent company to allow dealers to increase their repair and maintenance volume, but whatever it is, it should be re-examined. The customer is getting fed up with the high costs of repairs, suspicious of the dealer and his mechanics, and more and more prone to either attempt a do-it-yourself repair job or at least to find out for himself what is really wrong with his appliance. The television repair frauds prompted many states to enact stricter licensing and consumer protection laws. Many manufacturers advertise their service, but the actual performance is, in many cases, pitiful. In some instances the intentions of management are excellent, but the results not only turn the customer "off" but can be very costly to the company.

Sears

Sears reputation has been built on their "satisfaction guaranteed or your money back" policy. They do enforce it, and the customer can trust it. Sometimes it may prove to be rather expensive to the company.

A family ordered a small ice-maker freezer—sale price $139—from the Sears mail-order department. It was duly delivered after a six-week wait, but the freezer temperature would stay at 20-30 degrees F. just below freezing. A serviceman was called. He examined the freezer and decided that the condition was normal, and nothing could be done about it. As the specifications called for at least 0 degree coldness, another serviceman was sent by Sears. He spent quite a long time checking and diagnosed a faulty thermostat. This was ordered, and a month later, still another serviceman replaced the entire thermostat assembly. He was complaining that it took him so long to do it because, "those German units are very complicated"—the freezer is imported by Sears from Italy. But the change of thermostat did not improve the performance at all, so Sears politely and efficiently dispatched a fourth man, equipped with

an impressive array of equipment. Several hours later he added
Freon to a sealed unit that had to be opened and then soldered
shut. By then every piece of mechanism in the freezer was
examined, moved, replaced or otherwise tampered with. The
result was negative. A fifth repairman decided that he did not
know what was the matter with the freezer. By then the customer
took the "lemon" back to the Sears store, and after another
month, a brand new unit was delivered, installed and is operating
beautifully, making ice cubes at -10°F.

The moral of this story is obvious. The cost of sending five
servicemen to someone's home and the lengthy pseudo-repairs
must have cost Sears many times their projected profit on a $139
item. Why not replace the entire unit on the first call, or at least
on the second? Why not train repairmen better, particularly on
foreign-made equipment? Why not have a better control of service
calls to prevent unnecessary costs? And why subject a customer to
months and months of waiting and unsatisfactory operations? It is
obviously a combination of lack of control, faulty training and a
lack of individual decision making in exceptional cases. Sears will
not go out of business because of this incident, but it may be
symptomatic of incipient sloppiness and changing conditions. It
may be the clue for alert managements to start re-examining their
operations with a very critical look. Complacency is the most
dangerous management weakness in today's complex and churning
environment.

Green's Fuel Corp.

For years, Green's Fuel Corporation, a small owner-operated
propane gas distributor, serviced home customers in the Pompano
Beach, Florida, area. Its trucks would come and replenish gas
tanks either on a pre-set schedule or promptly after a telephone
call from a customer. The company was profitable; it had
satisfied customers and loyal and friendly employees. Texgas, a
United Texas Petroleum division and a subsidiary of Allied
Chemical, made an offer and gobbled up the small business in an
effort to extend its retail gas operations. And so Green's Fuel
became part of a large network whose headquarters were
thousands of miles away. Almost immediately the situation
changed. New policies were instituted—new rules, tighter budgets,
"big company" operations in a personalized service business.

Result: dissatisfied customers because of faulty deliveries, delays, unkept promises—in brief, a terrible deterioration of previously good service. Employees quit; several managers were hired and after a short time resigned or were fired. Tank-truck maintenance was reduced and trucks were breaking down with great regularity.

Here again the lessons are obvious. Absentee management by rules and procedures from far away does not provide the atmosphere and the close supervision required for good personalized service. This does not mean that only small, owner-operated companies can provide such service. It means that large companies have to learn how.

Airlines

Of all the "service" industries, the airlines used to pride themselves on their service concept. Millions of dollars of television advertising are directed to convince the flying public that the airlines "care" and bend backwards to please all the senses of their customers: gourmet foods, beverages, comfortable seats, attractive and hospitable stewardesses, prompt and good care of luggage, music and movies. But the airlines are also in deep financial troubles: high carrying charges and amortization of the new jets, increasing costs of operations, and leveling of demand contributed for many to a disastrous 1970 and even worse 1971 profit picture. Concurrently, and in many cases because of the profit squeeze, airlines began to neglect their number one asset and claim to uniqueness: passenger service. Many an experienced air traveller can recount increasing incidents of long lines at the ticket counters, inept handling of any exception by inexperienced and badly trained ground personnel, long waits for luggage and its brutal handling, deteriorating quality of cleanliness of the plane's cabin, and often rude behavior of the flying personnel, a long way from the fantasies and promises shown in advertisements and commercials.

American Airlines

A million-air-mile passenger, and a president of a corporation, on an American Airlines flight from Dallas to Tucson, asked the stewardess who was hustling drink orders for a tomato cocktail without alcohol. The girl yapped back something about "paying customers first." The passenger observed beforehand that the stewardess had some sort of a problem: she kicked luggage to fit it under the seat, snapped at another customer and behaved like a shrew, rather than the stereotyped sweet and smiling image. Trying to read a book and seeking to avoid any problems, the passenger ignored the girl's outburst. A few minutes later, she returned to ask passengers about their destination. The traveller replied with one word, "Tucson," upon which the stewardess threw a tantrum and loudly threatened him with bodily removal from the plane "because of his behavior!" Totally perplexed, the man kept calm and ignored the outburst, particularly since another passenger witnessed the scene and was also unable to understand the situation. The girl was obviously unfit, in her state of mind, to act as a stewardess on a crowded plane.

A letter requesting an apology from American Airlines brought, a month later, a vague mumbo-jumbo explanation, equivalent to a disinterested whitewash of the entire affair. The insulted executive tried to phone American Airlines headquarters in New York. Despite five attempts, he could never get beyond the secretaries and one junior administrative assistant. No executives could be reached, no messages were ever returned, and the entire attitude of the American Airlines executive suite was: "You're only a customer; don't bother us; you don't count."

Again the example is significant of the lack of understanding of consumerism by an important airline which used to be a pioneer in service and innovative techniques under the long rule of a real aviation man, C.R. Smith. Today's chief executive officer, Mr. George Spater, is a lawyer and probably a very good one. But his legal and impersonal way of running American Airlines is the exact contrary of what an airline needs to recapture the confidence of the customers. Ignoring service is going to hurt AA beyond the cold figures of the P&L. Despite a 5-year annual sales growth of 9.7%, the company's earnings per share show a decline of -37%, the worst 5-year results (together with Pan Am) of all 12 U.S. Airlines.

Whom can we trust?

Many corporations have let their services deteriorate and have incurred a growing customer resentment and dissappointment. But whether it was due to bad management and ignorance of the facts, or through deliberate moves to cut costs and achieve a short-range profit improvement, the actions were not designed to fraudulently fool and deceive the public. In many other instances, however, the growing wrath of the consumer is due to deliberate misrepresentations, calculated deceptions and a policy of "let's fool the public" on the part of large, "respectable" companies whose products are often household names and appear beyond reproach.

The Federal Trade Commission was never known for its prompt and efficient handling of customers' complaints. It is being forced, however, to move faster and more energetically because of the rising customer dissatisfaction and militancy.

Some of the cases handled by the FTC are quite revealing of the degree of advertising dishonesty and doubtful marketing practices of many companies on the select list of *Fortune*'s 500. The following are just a few examples of the dilemma of the average consumer who basically cannot and should not trust advertising claims.

Standard Oil Company of California

The FTC accused Standard Oil Company of California of falsely advertising that the "F-310" additive in its *Chevron* gasoline significantly reduces air pollution from auto exhausts. The complaint also cited *Chevron*'s advertising agency, Batten, Barton, Durstine & Osborn, Inc., New York City. In its proposed consent order, the FTC is demanding that any *Chevron* gasoline advertising in the next year clearly and conspicuously disclose that the FTC has found that the company's previous advertising for *Chevron* with F-310, which featured former astronaut Scott Carpenter, contained false, misleading and deceptive statements, representations and demonstrations, and that F-310 does not reduce air pollution.

Contrary to advertising claims, the FTC said, F-310 is not the most long-awaited gasoline development in history but is similar to additives found in other gasolines. The FTC also challenged these other claims: that *Chevron* with F-310 will significantly reduce air pollution from auto exhausts; that demonstrations with balloons and plastic bags pictured in advertising proved that F-310 will significantly reduce air pollution caused by auto; that every purchaser of *Chevron* with F-310 will obtain significantly better mileage; and that *Chevron* with F-310 will clean and help clean all engines and engine components. Furthermore, according to the FTC, a building labeled "Standard Oil Company of California Chevron Research Center" in the *Chevron* commercial was actually the County Court House in Palm Springs, California.

Standard Oil announced it will contest the FTC order and "will continue to market the product as aggressively as possible."

American Home Products

American Home Products Corporation, distributors of *Dristan* tablets, assured the Federal Trade Commission that it will not advertise that *Dristan* "will completely prevent or completely relieve all allergic symptoms," or that its use will enable one suffering from allergies "to lead completely the normal life of one who is not suffering from allergies." The drug firm also promised, in an assurance of voluntary compliance, not to suggest that the use of *Dristan* "is as effective as is avoidance of all the substance or substances to which one is allergic."

The FTC objected to such slogans as "*Dristan* tablets can make you feel like there is no pollen in the air," or "Now I can even chew on ragweed," and certain advertisements that portrayed a woman, supposedly allergic to roses, holding a rose to her nose.

Lever Brothers

In a new drive against faked television commercials, the FTC acted against two major sponsors. It obtained an affidavit of discontinuance from Lever Bros., New York City, of a commercial for *3B All* detergent in which an actor wearing a stained shirt pours some detergent into water rising around him as he stands fully dressed, apparently in some sort of tank. As the water recedes, the shirt appears to emerge free of its stain. The FTC said its investigation showed that the shirt had not been cleaned by the televised immersion, but by normal laundering.

Campbell Soup

A complaint against the Campbell Soup Co., Camden, N.J., charged that, in a TV commerical showing a bowl of soup rich in solid ingredients, the bowl was first filled with clear glass marbles "to prevent the solid ingredients ... from sinking" to the bottom. Campbell contended the commercial wasn't misleading but said it had stopped making commercials using the technique some months earlier after hearing from the FTC.

RCA

The RCA Corp. assured the Federal Trade Commission that it would drop some "Non-Smear Color TV" advertising claims. The ads, shown widely on television, claimed that RCA had developed a new transistorized tuner, and that "If you don't buy RCA, you may be buying an obsolete color TV." In the commercials, a split screen was used to demonstrate superior RCA reception. The RCA side of the picture was clear, the other blurred and distorted. The FTC said it learned, however, that the defects had been artificially created and that the RCA picture was not the result of a regular broadcast received by an actual television set.

The FTC said that, besides disparaging other brands, the commercials did not prove the quality of reception one would get with an RCA and consequently did not demonstrate any distinct superiority.

Geritol

A $1 million suit charging violations of a 1967 Federal Trade Commission order has been filed by the Justice Department against the companies that make and advertise *Geritol* and *FemIron.* The suit seeks $500,000 in civil damages from the J.B. Williams Co. and $500,000 from its advertising agency, Parkson Advertising Agency, Inc. It cited eleven alleged violations of a 1967 FTC order prohibiting false and misleading advertisements, including the claim that *Geritol Liquid, Geritol Tablets,* or *FemIron* are "a generally effective remedy of tiredness, loss of strength, run-down feelings, nervousness or irritability." The complaint was based on eleven different TV commercials shown in 1969.

General Foods

General Foods Corp. advertising for a drink called *Orange Plus* may have had a "tendency to convey the impression that certain fruit-flavored products were natural juices, contrary to fact," the Federal Trade Commission said. The big food-manufacturing firm signed an assurance of voluntary compliance, in which it said that it would disclose in advertising and on the label that the product is actually a frozen concentrate of imitation orange juice. Furthermore, General Foods promised not to disparage the nature or quality of any natural juice.

In another case, the Federal Trade Commission charged that General Foods and its advertising agency, Benton & Bowles, Inc., misrepresented *Toast 'ems* as containing at least as many nutrients as a breakfast of two eggs, two slices each of bacon and toast. General Foods signed an FTC consent order prohibiting it from making false nutritional claims for *Toast 'ems* or any other consumer food product.

Colgate-Palmolive

A television commercial for *Baggies,* a plastic wrap bag, sought to demonstrate its superior seal in a water test. But according to the Federal Trade Commission, "Dunking the sealed bags in a sink of water and swishing them vigorously for three to five seconds, during which time the closure of the competitive bag is forced open sufficiently to allow water to enter while no water enters the *Baggies,* is not evidence of the comparative abilities of the two bags to prevent food spoilage under ordinary conditions of use." The FTC charged that the demonstration was "false, misleading and deceptive."

The manufacturer, Colgate-Palmolive Co. of New York City, signed a consent order prohibiting the use of deceptive tests or demonstrations. The order also cited Colgate's advertising agency, Masius, Wynne-Williams, Street & Finney, Inc., also of New York City.

The Allstate Insurance Company, the nation's second largest automobile insurance company, is also forgetting the meaning of its motto, "You're in good hands with Allstate." A Delaware insurance official testified in a case that Allstate handled 19 percent of Delaware's car insurance business in 1969 but was the subject of 34 percent of the complaints to the state's insurance department about claims. A similar national opinion was found in a consumers' research magazine survey when Allstate was rated much poorer than average in most categories of service.

Few companies are immune from violations of public trust. ITT Continental Baking Co., makers of Profile bread, agreed to stop deceptive claims about slimming properties of their bread. Coca-Cola Co. was challenged that its Hi-C drinks are falsely advertised with regard to nutritional claims. Tire manufacturers are producing, at times, inferior and sub-standard tires and selling them to the unsuspecting public. Firestone Tire and Rubber Company, Mansfield Tire and Rubber Company, and Dunlop Tire and Rubber Corporation have been fined at various times for violations of the National Traffic and Motor Vehicle Safety Act of 1966.

The advertising industry

A great deal of blame for perpetrating deception on the consumer must be shared by the advertising industry. Advertising agencies are constantly looking for new gimmicks, new approaches, new ways to please their clients and to promote their products. The average life of an account is short, and the agency may lose a large percentage of their business at the slightest provocation or even without. Correspondingly, the life of an advertising executive is equally short, and he may often compromise his integrity for fear of losing his paycheck and his already shaky security.

It is difficult to understand how advertising agencies and their research departments are still underestimating the consumer and are considering him a Barnum-type sucker. A casual observation of commercials on television is enough to turn one's stomach, and yet the parade of testimonials, claims, and counter-claims appeals to the senses, and veiled threats keep blasting at the public at an increased rate, in vivid color.

The advertising industry leaders are guilty of the ostrich complex. Their short-term objectives for jungle survival must be totally overwhelming, as they don't see that they will bring on themselves a whole battery of state and federal regulations and controls if the present practices continue. The consumer is becoming disgusted, suspicious, and above all, active rather than passive. Deceptive advertising will be his prime target.

It is also difficult to visualize the lack of sensitivity on this subject on the part of the corporations. Their sales will ultimately suffer from exposure of the deceptions, and yet the pressures for sales volume and share of the market must be so great as to neglect the future for immediate results. "Apres moi, le deluge," seems to be the favorite mottos of the modern day marketing executives.

Where do we stand?

The U.S. has 60 percent of its non-agricultural, non-governmental work force employed in the service industry. Thus we can lay claim to be the world's first service economy. We also can claim to be the world's worst-served economy. In large measure the troubles of the service industry are due to the attempts to match wage standards set by the highly productive manufacturing industries, which can automate and realize economies of mass production and assembly-line methods. Thus service industries usually have to cut their service because of inadequate profits or sub-standard personnel. Also, their standards for "quality control" are primitive or non-existent.

The disappointing performance of service industries is an open invitation for a consumer revolt, and the rise of consumerism is due, to a great degree, to the lack of or grossly inferior service, when the customer paid for and was entitled to a better treatment.

The manufacturing sector is also showing a disappointing and short-sighted attitude toward the consumer. There is a noticeable decline in the quality of products. Even the most reputable companies, with long histories of quality products, are slipping. Again, rising costs, and thus attempts at short-cuts and increasing indifference of the employees, contribute to the quality slippage.

As quality slips, the advertising claims get louder, deceptive, and in some cases, fraudulent. And such actions are not perpetrated by small, shoddy, fly-by-night enterprises, but by the cream and the elite of our industrial corporations.

Should this situation continue, the reaction will come swifter than expected. Already the consumer is rebelling. Ralph Nader's impact was greater than anyone had predicted. The federal government has not only passed additional consumer protection laws, but is finally beginning to enforce the laws and is putting teeth into the operation of agencies charged with consumer protection. Companies that do not modify their attitudes and policies will suffer—and rightly so.

What should be done?

Corporate policy should be dictated by common sense and a basic attitude of fairness toward their customers. Common sense would dictate the following policies:

(1) General recognition that "consumerism is in reality a strong and important force in our present economy. It must be considered as one of the dominant forces.

> This cannot be a passive or a token acceptance. It must be fully understood within the "guts" of the executive, even if he dislikes the whole idea and would rather put it out of his mind.

(2) Recognition that consumerism is here, not only to stay, but as basically a force for the good and not a threat to business enterprises.

As a pragmatic realist, a modern executive should not gear himself to "fight" consumerism, to try to circumvent its demands by gimmicks or trickery. Consumerism is not "an evil subversive force fomented by left-wing radicals to undermine our free enterprise system," as some stubborn businessmen may imply. On the contrary, the consumer is beginning to apply the purest principles of a true competitive system: he chooses what he wants to buy.

(3) Communicate the acceptance and recognition of consumerism as a positive force all the way down in the organization.

Your people must honestly believe that the top management is not only aware of the new facts of life, but is not directing them to fight it. The downward communication must be carefully designed to impress the "troops" with the sincerity of top management's feelings—not a sugarcoated public relations placebo.

(4) Devise within the corporation positive action plans to cope with consumerism and to profit by it. These plans will be extensive and permeate all phases of a business operation, because the indirect ramifications of such actions reach throughout every department of the company.

A. Personnel Plans: (a) *Training:* Intensive and dedicated training that "service" is not dead in the U.S.A. and the company that would give service will take a leading advantage over its competitors. Even if costs are higher, the consumer, less price conscious and more service and quality oriented, will, in the long run, swing to the "good service company." The training, or perhaps retraining, of people will be the hardest task. During the years, many bad habits have been acquired and tolerated: rudeness, indifference, lack of loyalty, lack of pride in the tasks performed, and sometimes even deliberate attempts to hurt the employer. (b) *Incentives:* Training, communications, exhortations and explanations will not suffice. They can only lay the groundwork and prepare the employee. His performance in that direction must further be rewarded by an incentive plan geared to his results. Profit sharing, bonuses, higher pay, extra benefits, various stock options, or paid vacation travel are some of the numerous tangible incentives, each with almost infinite variations. There are experts in the field to recommend the most suitable plan for the company's particular situation. Personnel managers are cognizant of these, but often nobody listens to them. Whatever the source of the plan, the fact remains that an incentive system that will reward highly for service and quality is a must in today's and tomorrow's economy.

B. Quality Control: There are innumerable examples of drastic deterioration of quality of products in our country. One could cite examples in every sector of production. Once greatly reliable Diesels are delivered with loose screws in the pistons, necessitating complete replacement by the manufacturer and causing a boat owner months of delays and inconveniences after the initial installation. Automobiles are delivered with loosely attached parts that jam or fall out, causing damage or even danger to the proud new-car owner. Appliances don't work and the dealer is unable to repair them. Sometimes a paradox occurs. A large and leading television manufacturer shipped thousands upon thousands of brand new "solid state" television sets to his dealers. There was a defect in the tuner circuitry. During a recent slump in color television sales, the dealer was making a greater profit by charging the manufacturer his regular service rate to repair the new sets in stock than from his actual sales to customers. A hospital used to get excellent results by letting the technicians check the Pap Tests for cervical cancer. The pathologist would examine one in ten samples to statistically verify the technicians' work. In recent times, different work force, different attitudes, and different conditions have caused such a deterioration of quality of testing that after several diagnosis errors, the hospital is revising its sample checking procedure to assure the same results as in the past. The food industry is in a turmoil revising their quality control methods, due to the incidence of botulism and food contamination due to sloppy handling. Past quality methods are providing inadequate for today's conditions. Thus, a thorough investigation and most probably revision of a company's quality control procedures in all phases of operations is a must. In many cases it will not only help the business operate better and more profitably, but may save the company from bankruptcy, as in the case of the 100-years-old Bon Vivant Soup Company.

C. Consumer Communication and Feedback: It is becoming increasingly important to understand the changing mood of the consumer, and particularly one's customer. Many corporations have created new positions of Vice-President or Director of Customer Relations, apart from Public Relations. Insurance companies like Travelers, car manufacturers like Ford and American Motors, and many others across the country have instituted "we listen and we care" programs. These are intended to bring the company in closer contact with the customer, provide the company with the grass-roots direct feel of the situation, and also to allow some avenue of communication to the frustrated and often unhappy customer.

In theory the programs sound good, and the objective is certainly laudable. In reality, it is still often either a window dressing for public relations propaganda or a most ineffectual administrative boondoggle. Many readers who have ever had a billing error or adjustment with any large credit card companies can vouch to their frustrations when trying to contact their credit card company representative or writing explanatory letters. You cannot get the representative on the phone, your messages are unanswered and your letters are ignored. Often, people's credit ratings were hurt or unnecessary embarrassment was suffered because of the credit card companies' errors and inability to correct them.

The same lack of customer service occurs with Hertz, the self-proclaimed service company. Cars are dirty, many features are inoperative (cigarette lighters, windshield wipers, radios, and even starters) and you may get billed twice or three times after you duly paid the original invoice. The funniest incident occurred in Florida with an Avis rented car. The car stalled and would not start. A card conspicuously placed inside stated that in case of any malfunction to call a certain number, toll free, and immediate attention will be given to the problem. The customer called the number, only to be told by the operator that such number did not exist. The man could not believe it and repeated the procedure with another operator to make sure he gave her the printed number. Same diagnosis. Either the printing was wrong or the service had been discontinued.

The Whirlpool corporation has a Watts number for toll-free calls from customers having either problems or wishing information about the Whirlpool appliances. A customer tried to call the number fifteen times in one day at various times, hoping to get some information about his new, highly advertised *Trashmasher*. The line was busy. Millions of dollars of expensive advertising will not make him buy another Whirlpool appliance.

These are just a few examples of the ineptness of handling the new "fad" of consumer relations. It cannot be considered a fad or a window dressing. It must become a reliable two-way communication device between the customer and the company, with benefits for both. Actually, highly touted but badly operating consumer relations departments are worse than none. It is expensive to the company and creates more bad will than when they had no such function.

(5) Do not forget to also devise, in conjunction with the new plans for personnel training and incentives, improved quality control, and consumer relations dialogue, a positive and strict system of controls. The company's management must know rapidly and accurately how the implementation of these plans, and any other plans, is proceeding. Is the implementation schedule on target, are the cost estimates holding up, and above all, are the results up to predetermined new norms? In an era of greater permissiveness, we must face a general condition of looser and sloppier performance. Thus, controls become more important than ever. The feedback is not only essential, but probably its frequency should be increased. In the same vein, the reaction time to a problem discovered through the feedback should be decreased. In brief, we need to discover our errors faster and correct them faster, or the program or even the company will be in serious trouble faster than in the past.

Consumer pressure, combined with governmental regulations, is here to stay and will increase. Any company, large or small, can either fight or ignore it and lose—or constructively and honestly devise a new way to capitalize on the new situation and win.

LESSONS TO BE LEARNED

(1) Consumerism is here to stay. You can't ignore it, fight it or control it.

(2) Don't underestimate the consumer. He is not a "sucker" with a child's mentality. He is more educated, more selective and less gullible than in the past.

(3) Promises or pretty design will not compensate for lack of service. USA is a service economy, and the consumer will demand service and seek out companies that genuinely try to provide it.

(4) Don't deceive the consumer. Governmental and other agencies will step up review and enforcement of exposure and prosecution of false and often fraudulent claims.

(5) The advertising industry—Madison Avenue—the television networks, the "creative and imaginative" marketeers will have to curb their flights of fancy to stick more with the truth and the facts. The public is demanding it and is entitled to it.

(6) Companies must start considering consumerism as a positive and a constructive force. Their internal policies must be geared to profit by it, not to deplore it.

(7) Personnel training to provide efficient and courteous service must be instituted and accelerated.

(8) Better quality control methods and higher standards must be devised and adhered to.

(9) New incentives for employees are necessary to encourage and reward their attention to consumerism and consumers.

(10) Better, more honest and more sincere two-way communications must be established between customers and suppliers. A truthful feedback of consumer feelings must be devised all the way up to the top management—on a current and comprehensive basis.

Chapter 17

COMPUTERS: USE BUT DON'T MISUSE

"In terms of technical achievement, the computer revolution in the U.S. has been outrunning all expectations. In terms of economic payoff on new applications, it has rapidly lost momentum."
    —"The Arts of Top Management"
        McKinsey & Company

"Management's romance with computers for their own sake is over. New systems must justify their cost and performance."
        —"Business Takes a Second Look
            at Computers"
                Business Week

"What companies 'have done' shade into 'what we are now doing' which leads to 'what we plan to do' next year."
    —National Association of Accountants

"For the most part, third generation equipment is being used on systems with second-generation design."
        —"The Computer Comes of Age"
            Booz, Allen and Hamilton, Inc.

Most of us know through personal involvement some inconvenience or expense that can be traced to the failure of the computer. Every manager has a classic story of a particular "goof up" caused by a computer. Most of these stories are funny. They range from the incident of the little old lady in Iowa and her million dollar tax refund to the case of Penn Central Railroad, who literally *lost* entire trains and hundreds of boxcars. These experiences are not so funny to those on the receiving end. The frustration caused by these computer errors is typified by William Fine, President of New York's Bonwit Teller: "I wish I could put my arms around every customer our computers screw up and say, 'there, there, we'll figure a way between us to make the computer cry, just for once.' "

Stories such as these reflect a curious dichotomy in American business. On the one hand we have the growing necessity to use these machines to improve the management of complex operations. Moreover, there is the accelerating rate of dollars spent on them. In 1970 alone, *$25 billion*—2 percent of the gross national product—was spent in the United States on computers and operating staffs. Computer hardware alone is expected to shortly exceed 15 percent of expenditures for new plant and equipment.

On the other hand, the computer honeymoon is over, and businessmen are increasingly disillusioned with them. This is due, in part, to the economic shakeout of 1969-71—a shakeout that separated the men from the boys in more areas than just computer operations.

While transforming clerical and accounting operations, computers have had surprisingly little impact on the operating problems of management, the area where the real payoff potential lies. Meanwhile, the gap between the potential of the computer and its actual achievement continues to widen as the stakes and costs keep rising. From a profit standpoint, computer efforts in all but a few exceptional companies (eg., Pillsbury, Weyerhaeuser, Westinghouse) appear to be in trouble. Third and fourth generation hardware, more costly staffs, and increasingly complex operations can be found everywhere. However, much less in evidence is the *computer application that is profitable*. Sometimes the manager is faced with a curious choice: "Damned if I do and damned if I don't!"

The problem

The problem is to obtain economic payoffs from the computer. Failure to do this can generally be traced to four causes:

Management system vs. information system

A lot of managers think that an *information system* will substitute for a *management system.* Nothing could be further from the truth. If good planning and control doesn't exist within the framework of a good organization, then no degree of sophistication with a computer is going to have a payoff.

The lack of *managerial* and *operational* applications (as opposed to accounting or clerical) is a serious problem, because this lack implies that the process of management *(planning and control)* is not being performed well. If we say, as we must, that information is the raw material of decision making, and if information is not being generated, disseminated, and *used,* then no system, *manual or computer*, is going to help.

Litton was known far and wide for its sophisticated, *expensive* management information system. Roy Ash was asked by President Nixon to chair the committee for structuring an information system for the U.S. Government. However, for a variety of reasons (mostly those surrounding conglomeration) Litton's backup *management system* didn't withstand the economic shakeout, and consequently the information system and the computers had minimum payoff.

Moral: Have good management first and then the computer may help to improve operations.

Managerial involvement

Of all the reasons for the failure of computer systems, *lack of managerial involvement* heads the list. Remember: computers are too important to be left to computer technicians. In his very clever book, *Up the Organization,* Robert Townsend concluded: "They (the computer technicians) are trying to make it look tough. Not easy. They're building a mystique, a priesthood, their own mumbo-jumbo ritual to keep you from knowing what they—and you—are doing."

Look at Weyerhaeuser's success with computers. This success is attributed directly to the fact that George Weyerhaeuser, the president, took a personal interest and participated directly in defining what work he wanted computers to do for the company. Look at any company that is successful with profitable computer applications, and you will find the same thing: Managerial *(and we mean chief executive)* involvement.

Communication gap

We have a long way to go before the computer can talk management's language, and managers, by and large, are not about to talk the language of the computer (or computer technicians). The result—a communication gap!

On the one hand we have the technician or the analyst who has little concept of the process of management or of the problems of managers. Operation of the machine is their "thing," and their objective is frequently seen in terms of processing speed or pages of output. They bamboozle the manager/user with such terms as: "35K . . . accessing speed . . . source data automation . . . input format, etc." They have little knowledge of, or interest in, how the information is used to improve operations.

On the other hand we have the managers. Unless he's been to a "B" school or a good seminar recently, he is likely to be unknowledgeable and therefore apprehensive about the computer. The result: abdication to the technician.

Moral: Retread your managers through management development.

Organization

In some respects it is unfortunate that when computers burst upon the business scene 10-15 years ago, the only practical applications at that time were concerned with the automation of clerical work: accounting, payroll, and similar jobs. Following the classical organizational principle of assignment by familiarity, the overwhelming trend at the time was to assign the computer to the controller or the chief accountant. Generally, that is where it has remained. The result has been a disproportionate emphasis on accounting and other clerical work. This development is only natural because the computer gave the controller an added dimension of importance, and it is too much to expect that he would share it with any *line* or *operational* manager.

Rare is the company that has a vice-president who is knowledgeable in and responsible for the *information function*. Fortunately, a rapidly growing number of well-managed firms realize the importance of this function and are assigning it *to* or *near* the chief executive.

Moral: Organize for management information systems.

The don'ts of computer use

Here are a few don'ts that the *manager*—and the technician—should remember:

Don't Buy a "Turnkey" Operation

Some computer manufacturers and some consultants will try to sell you the "turnkey" system—one that is designed and debugged and ready for you to "push the button" or "turn the key." Warning: Don't buy it! First, the chances are good that you will nave to spend a lot of time educating *him* in *your* operations. Second, installing the system without substantial preparation is likely to result in chaos. Third, if you don't have the capable staff to design your own systems, it is unlikely that the same staff can operate it after it's "installed" by the consultant.

One company that did some costly floundering before settling down to some good computer systems is Borden, Inc. The advice of the vice-president in charge is: "If you don't have an in-house staff doing the job of design and also available to maintain it, you are asking for trouble."

Moral: Systems are much more likely to work if you design them yourself.

Don't Spend All Your Money on Hardware

The average breakdown for each dollar of computer expenditures is hardware 35¢, staff 30¢, updating present system 15¢, and new applications 20¢. These *new application* dollars are the only computer outlays subject to significant short-term management control. Yet their leverage on future costs and benefits is enormous. Indeed, these costs hold the key to any future improvement in operational management due to computer development.

Moral: Spend more on new applications and development.

Don't let Computer Salesman and Data Processing Managers Make Computer Decisions

Both of these guys are like foxes who like to eat chickens! Their natural inclination is to promise everything without too much regard for delivery. Remember, the machine is their "bag"—not how to improve management. So even if they both are honest, you will be oversold almost every time.

Moral: Beware the primrose path offered by the specialist.

Don't Try to Install an MIS Without an MS

To repeat—you can't have an *information system* unless it is built on the foundation of a good *management system*. Let's combine these:

MANAGEMENT SYSTEM	MANAGEMENT INFORMATION SYSTEM
Plan	The company that has success in profitable MIS applications is the company that *plans* for MIS . . . period!
Organize	To use an analogy—organization is the anatomy of the company, and the MIS is the nervous system. Organize for MIS.
Control	Assign a measure of performance to your MIS. If its objective is to improve inventory turnover by 20 percent—does it do this?

Moral: Build an MIS on top of a management system that includes the organizational arrangements, the structure and procedures for adequate planning and control, the clear establishment of objectives, and all the other manifestations of good organization and management.

Don't Fall in Love with Your System

Remember Ford's Edsel? Remember General Dynamic's Convair? Remember when Perlman of New York Central merged with Saunders of Pennsylvania and neither would budge an inch on their individual computer systems? All of these people became "locked in" to a losing proposition. Although they knew the ship was sinking they insisted on going down with it.

Moral: If the system doesn't work, scrap it before you lose more money.

Don't Underestimate the Time and
Expense of Developing a System

The inclination of systems people and "computercrats" is to underestimate the time and cost for developing and installing a system by a factor of 50-90 percent.

Moral: *Beware.* Cost, time and efficiency overruns are bad news! The credibility of the company is at stake, to say nothing of cost.

The do's of computer use

Now for some do's:

Do Get Management Involved

Dozens of studies on hundreds of companies involving thousands of executives have concluded: The most striking characteristic of the successful company is that MIS development has been viewed as a responsibility of management. This includes both top management and operating line management. Even the federal government concluded: "Without question, the single most critical problem in effective computer utilization is the need for understanding and support of top management."

Moral: *Management involvement* in systems design is essential for closing the communication gap and getting profitable applications.

Do Eyeball the Output

A computer credits a New York taxi driver's bank account with $1 million. Chrysler's computer ships thousands of cars to the wrong destination. The Army's computer orders 18 thousand dozen shirts, size 18. These are typical boners caused by the inability of computers to exercise human judgment. Yet this judgment is frequently so necessary. Consider, for example, the allocation of overhead to plants and divisions made automatically by computer. Shouldn't the printout be "eyeballed?" Shouldn't the division manager be able to complain about the "programmed" decision and get an adjustment in a human way?

Moral: Eyeballing can catch expensive, embarrassing mistakes.

Do Upgrade Your Clerical Systems

Hundreds of opportunities exist to redesign and upgrade systems for *managerial* and *operational* uses. For example:

Clerical System		Management System
Ledger Accounting	*becomes*	Financial Planning
Order Entry and Billing	*becomes*	Sales Analysis and Market Research
Inventory Accounting	*becomes*	Inventory Management
Production Reporting	*becomes*	Production Planning and Control

Moral: Check your *clerical* systems for possible *managerial* and *decision-making* applications.

Do Put Proposed Projects to the Feasibility Test

Remember that the *raison d'être* of an information system is to help solve problems, and before approving new or modified applications ask yourself:

Is it *technically* feasible?—Is it practical within the scope of our available technology and resources?

Is it *economically* feasible?—Does it have a payoff and will it return more money than it costs?

Is it *operationally* feasible?—Will the system be used, or will it be resisted and ignored?

Moral: Make sure a system is feasible before you buy it.

Do Develop an MIS Plan

The reasons for MIS planning are the same as for planning in general:

Planning offsets uncertainty.
Planning improves economy of operations.
Planning focuses on objectives.
Planning provides a device for control of operations.

Without a plan, the result is likely to be a patchwork approach that will result in "islands of mechanization" with no integration.

The key question is not so much "How are we doing?" but "Where are we heading?" Until now, record keeping and accounting (payroll is 50 percent of computer time in a lot of companies) were the bulk of applications. However, if you want to upgrade your systems into *decision making* and *managerial* applications, it is essential that a plan be developed and that manager/users be involved in it.

Another point—participation in planning will serve to help overcome the most difficult roadblock to MIS implementation—organizational resistance.

Moral: The time for MIS planning is now!

How to design a system*

Automation of paperwork—the usual approach of the technician—is sometimes called the *perpetuation of inefficiency at an accelerating rate*. If you want to avoid this approach and get profitable applications, you should be prepared to participate in 'and guide systems design; it isn't that hard to do.

Set system objectives

This is an obvious step so frequently overlooked or misstated. Such statements as "get the report out on time" or "keep accurate records" are not adequate. Objectives must be stated in terms of what the user expects to achieve, and these attempt to answer the questions: What is the purpose of the system? Why is it needed? What is it expected to do? To illustrate: production control might be, "Identify cost variances within one day in order to control overruns;" sales analysis might be, "Segment customers by size and order frequency in order to direct sales effort."

Identify constraints

In most cases you will have to back down from the "ideal" system because of constraints or restrictions. These are *external*

---

*For the manager who is really serious about improving computer operations, we recommend a book written by one of the authors. See, Joel E. Ross, *Management by Information Systems,* Prentice-Hall, Inc., 1970.

(customer, supplier, legal, etc.) and *internal* (management support, manpower, cost, organizational acceptance, time, etc.). Whatever the constraint, it had better be identified in the early stages or expensive rework will be necessary. In general, technicians only consider technical (machine) constraints.

Determine information needs

The real reason for having an information system is to provide the information in order to meet the objective. This is why both the objective and the information needs must be stated in specifics, not generalities. The computer won't accept generalities.

Using the two examples above, the stated objectives might be met with the following information needs: production control could be, "Daily exception report to identify by shop order and lot number the variances in cost and quantity that are over or under by 5 percent."

Information sources

Ask the question: Where do I obtain the information to meet the needs in order to achieve system objective? The answer requires an analysis of existing books, records, files, statistical and accounting documents, and other internal sources. Perhaps a new form will be required. Up to this step the manager has had little need for the analyst. Perhaps he should be called in at this step.

System concept

This step is generally involved with data flow—*inputs* (in what form do we get the information into the computer) and outputs (what does the information look like when it comes out of the computer). Since the output provides your information needs and is the real reason for having the system, it is of utmost importance to the manager/user. Ask the questions: What form are the output reports to take? Should the information be detailed or summarized? What is the output form? Are reports generated on demand, by exception, on schedule?

This step cannot be abdicated.

Test and implement the system

The important thing to remember here is that the old system should not be closed down and discarded before the new one is operational and *proven*. Nightmarish stories abound throughout industry about computer-based information systems that have flopped. If this should happen to yours, it's nice to know that you have the old system to return to.

Chapter 18

ACCOUNTING MANIPULATIONS: YOU CAN'T FOOL EVERYBODY FOR LONG

> "Give me the books of almost any company and within a year's time I can double earnings."
> —Partner, "Big Eight" Accounting Firm
>
> "You don't have to be in our business very long before you realize that what most companies call their earnings can be almost anything they want them to be.
> —Head of Leading Wall Street Firm

Commencing in January of any year, outside auditors begin combing through the financial records of the great corporations throughout the nation—verifying, cross-checking, questioning. It is annual audit time and all publicly-held companies must open their books to inspection by independent accountants. Later in the year, each annual financial statement will carry the customary certificate, signed by a certified public accountant, stating that the statement has been prepared "in accordance with generally accepted accounting principles."

On the basis of these audited financial statements the general investing public will make billions of dollars of investment decisions, lending institutions will decide who is a bad risk and who will get a loan, and corporate top managements will be judged smart or dumb. *Is it any wonder that the temptation to manipu-*

late the financial statement is so great? And what does it all add
up to? Stated simply, it adds up to a lot of trouble. A majority of
annual reports must be read with skepticism. Many are outright
deceptive. Only a minority are frank and honest. Some border on
dishonesty.

The question arises, who's at fault for the publication of
financial statements that are something less than honest and
factual? Is it the public, or is it the corporate managers? The
public insists on a distilled, single, absolute figure that represents
the results of an entire year's operation of a huge business
enterprise. This figure is *net earnings.* It has a magical signifi-
cance—not only to the ordinary investor, but to the security
analysts, the stockholders, and the acquisition-minded manager as
well. On the reliability of the *earnings per share* figure, billions of
investment dollars are wagered.

Perhaps the accounting profession is at fault. Are they not
independent professionals and can they not arrive at precise
figures based upon commonly accepted principles? The answer, of
course, is yes—and no! Generally, three reasons are given to
absolve the accounting profession: (1) accounting principles are
not clearly defined and, therefore, a number of ways exist to
handle the same item; (2) the relationship between the auditor and
the corporation is not impartial since the client (corporation) pays
the accountant's fee; and (3) accounting is not yet a profession in
the sense that it is independent of its customers.

However, in the last analysis, neither the public nor the
accountants can be blamed for accounting manipulation. But,
corporate management *can* be blamed.

Where there is more than one way to report expenses and
earnings (and there almost always is), nobody can blame the
manager for giving himself the benefit of the doubt. On the other
hand, there is no excuse for corporate managers to take advantage
of accounting loopholes in order to hide behind the facts for the
purpose of misinforming the public or the stockholders.

Accounting statements: their use and misuse

Although the ostensible purpose of an annual report is to truly
reflect the financial condition of the company during the year just
ended, the report is frequently used for other purposes. Foremost
among these is its promotional uses, an exercise in corporate

vanity. The report not only informs the shareholders that the company has gone through another year without going bankrupt, but it also enables company management to give credit where credit is due—namely, to company management.

As a financial reporting device, the accounting statements (annual reports) are rather technical and can be prepared in short order by professional accountants. However, since their primary use has become promotional their annual preparation has become more of a corporate ritual fire dance. Everybody—including the very top management—is in there pitching. Text must be written, figures obtained, pictures gathered, layout prepared, and everything must be revised, edited, checked, and re-checked. And the result? You can usually rely on the correctness of the company's address. Too often, the annual reports simply fail to report. Beyond its polysyllabic rhetoric and philosophical prose, aside from its racy photography and mod styling, many reports give disproportionate coverage to the small amount of cheerful news while painting over the uncomfortable or embarrassing facts. The real story is more often found in the footnotes that are hard to discover, difficult to read, and sometimes impossible to understand.

Cause of manipulative disease

Manipulative accounting is contagious. It is also easy to trace.

The disease was particularly rampant in the late sixties when the idea was created and widely accepted that it was possible to create earnings curves that could rise in unbroken lines, apparently forever. If a company could persuade the investing public of this fact (or fiction), then the public would place a high premium on such ascending curves in terms of stock prices. Those companies whose curves were flat or fluctuating were generally sneered at by the public; such a company was hit where it hurts the most: *right in their price/earnings ratio.*

Those cyclical or other companies with flat or fluctuating earnings curves were bringing about ten times earnings in the stock market. Those with the sweeping-up curves could expect to go for thirty, forty, or even fifty times earnings.

It doesn't take much imagination to figure out what this will do for *stock options* held by management. And what about those juicy *acquisitions* of companies with low multiples? Isn't it a matter of *corporate prestige* to maintain a high price/earnings ratio?

The disease got so bad with some company managements that they began to view the maintenance of a high price/earnings ratio as the corporate objective, rather than cash flow and profit from operations.

The next phase of the manipulative disease followed naturally. Imaginative managers began to do things with their books so that it would appear to the investing public that they, too, had an ascending earnings curve—even if they really didn't. As the myth of such false earnings became more widely accepted by an uncritical public, the rewards of "imaginative" accounting became greater and the disease fed on itself. The contagion became an epidemic. Sound, businesslike managements came down with the disease because they almost had to. Their existence was threatened by the acquisition-minded companies whose managements knew how to use high price/earnings stock to take over low price/earnings companies. As the big conservative companies sought ways to check the takeover boys, they themselves began to utilize some of the questionable practices of manipulation. Hence, many steel companies changed from accelerated to the straight-line method of depreciation, adding millions of dollars to reported earnings. In the hard-pressed airline industry, companies stretched out depreciation on jet aircraft. Many companies switched from last-in, first-out inventory to first-in, first-out in order to improve reported earnings. However, these bookkeeping switches were mild in comparison to methods used by others. All of them amounted to nothing more than borrowing from future earnings, and accounting manipulators were to eventually get their comeuppance.

Results of the manipulative disease

While the manipulation of the accounts may improve *reported* (not actual) earnings in the short run, the use of this method will only delay the inevitable. As one old hard-bitten tycoon, a veteran of dozens of acquisitions, said, "When they come to me with a company and say, 'Look at that earnings growth, up X percent every year,' I say to myself, 'And I know why your company is for sale: it's on the brink; you've used up all the credits you had.' "

Using up future credits, delaying depreciation, capitalizing expenses, overstating goodwill, putting capital gains into operating income—all of these are accounting techniques that, while technically correct, merely delay the day of reckoning. And, when the day of reckoning comes, it can mean disaster. "Creative bookkeeping" amounts to little more than borrowing from future earnings, and the company that squeezes big mileage out of favorable accounting options may find that the same options will work against them at the day of reckoning. As the financial vice-president of the troubled University Computing Company remarked: "You can push these things forward, but eventually they come home to roost."

The comic conglomerates

If an enterprising cartoonist wanted to start a comic strip about the business world, he would very likely choose the conglomerates. The men who managed these companies were master manipulators of the books. Many of them were run by boy geniuses with a brilliant financial plan: Take over bigger and more solid companies by issuing debt whose carrying charges would come from the earnings of the company acquired. And, of course, the acquiring company would have all kinds of opportunities for "creative bookkeeping."

The conglomerate managers found to their chagrin that the shrewdness, imagination, and gall that make a man an empire builder do not make him a skilled manager. In general they failed to realize until it was too late that an earnings curve developed through fast bookkeeping must ultimately be supported and maintained through operations. When it came time to make a profit through operations, many of the go-go conglomerators found that the earnings that had been borrowed in the past were now past due. As one Wall Street analyst concluded, "In the past, a lot of these companies squeezed big mileage out of favorable accounting options. But, now the same options are working *against* them." A few examples will serve to illustrate.

Westec

In 1965, Westec Corporation's acquisition-minded management provided the lesson that was to be ignored by dozens of imitators. In order to keep earnings and the price of its stock as high as possible, Westec had been pushing the manipulative accounting principles to the breaking point. They treated oil production payments as current income rather than deferring them until the oil was actually produced. They took directly into income non-recurring profits on sales of oil properties. They took into earnings for a given year profits of companies not acquired until the following year. Just nine months after reporting 1965 earnings of $4.9 million and assets of $56 million, Westec was in bankruptcy. Despite all of this, several of the most respected accounting firms pointed out that Westec had not exceeded any accounting rules.

Litton

Litton Industries was the grandaddy of all conglomerates and for a long time was a legend—a legend of sixteen years of unbroken growth that took the company from $3 million in sales in 1953 to over $2 billion in 1969. And earnings kept pace until the inevitable payoff was due; the payoff from manipulating the books in order to maintain a spectacular record of growth in earnings which in turn would lead to a high price/earnings ratio.

The investing public, and seemingly the management of Litton, was not too concerned with the nature of the firm's business, or what products they manufactured and sold. Instead, Litton's management talked concepts and systems and the technologies of tomorrow. Synergism, growth, and financial manipulation was the output of the company, and the investing public ate it up. This kind of philosophy helped win Litton a sky-high price/earnings ratio. This, in turn, facilitated acquisitions on favorable terms. Predictably, this practice was ultimately to backfire. What became abundantly clear was the considerable distance between concept and reality at Litton. When earnings inevitably slipped, the bubble burst. Litton's stock went from 120 to 10.

The first sag in earnings occurred in 1968. It was accompanied by a substantial stock price slide. The management of the company decided that earnings must recover at all costs. And they did in 1969 by 35 percent *apparently*. This apparent recovery was accomplished by a clever bit of accounting manipulation. In an interesting *footnote* to the financial statement, it was revealed that Litton had included in *operating* earnings a $23.2 million capital gain on sale of McLean Industries stock. A capital gain in operating earnings? Not really, because in its nine-month earnings report of the same year, the same amount, $23.2 million, had been set up as a "reserve" for start-up costs in Litton's shipyard. As luck would have it, the $23.2 million loss did occur, but was never reported as a reduction in earnings. In summary, a non-recurring capital gain was used to offset an *operating* loss and stockholders will never be the wiser unless they read the fine print very, very carefully.

Ling-Temco-Vought

The most imaginative "bookkeeper" of them all was James J. Ling, Chairman of LTV. We have already seen (Chapter 7) how his "redeployment of assets" strategy permitted the pyramidding of acquisitions.

An example of Jim Ling's bookkeeping talents can be demonstrated in the case of Computer Technology, an LTV acquisition. Despite the fact that in 1968 Computer Technology earned only 11 cents per share, the public bid the price of the stock up as high as 42-1/2—a phenomenal *386 to 1 price/earnings multiple.* What was even more remarkable was the fact that about two-thirds of Computer Technology's "earnings" of 11 cents a share came from *a contract with LTV*—the parent. However, as with most cases of accounting manipulation, this one eventually came home to roost. The price of Computer Technology stock went below 3 and a lawsuit was launched against LTV, charging that the LTV-UCC deal was milking Computer Technology stockholders.

Another recent interesting footnote in LTV's financial statement concerned its subsidiary, Jones and Laughlin Steel. Although J&L reported a loss to the IRS, it reported a $22 million profit in the annual statement. However, $13 million of the profit was from the sale of future production of material deposits at a discount; in other words, J&L took a profit today for something that it would produce later on.

Some people will do anything to improve that earnings curve, but the day of reckoning inevitably arrives.

Other comic conglomerates

Not to be outdone by their big brothers, the smaller conglomerates also resorted to "creative bookkeeping" in their
acquisition binges.

> *Item.* In a recent annual statement of Studebaker-Worthington
> (S-W), no less than four separate figures were shown for earnings
> per share. These ranged from $5.01 down to $2.76, despite the
> fact that the lower figure would reflect a substantial earnings
> downturn. However, the company claimed an unbroken rise in
> earnings per share since the pre-merger days of 1964.
>
> *Item.* Giffen Industries bought 51 percent of Keller Industries for
> $49.8 million. A postmerger audit revealed that Keller's pre-
> merger earnings were $1.50 and not the $2.63 claimed. Keller's
> defense was that Giffen officials were in such a hurry that they
> refused an offer to inspect his books.
>
> *Item.* GAC Corporation—one of the giant land development
> companies—was flying high in the bull market of 1967-68. Its
> stock hit a high of 67-1/2. The slide was inevitable because like
> many land companies, GAC recorded as *current profit* the
> earnings from land sales contracts even though the down payment
> went largely to the salesman. The profit, if any, was to be payable
> over a long period of years.
>
> *Item.* Liquidonics Industries ($54 million sales) possessed hold-
> ings of UMC Corporation ($134 million sales) and borrowed $56
> million to complete the takeover. However, it couldn't complete
> the acquisition because the loan gave them such a huge debt/
> equity ratio that the interest could not be paid. To make matters
> worse, if it sells its UMC holdings to get cash, it would incure a
> $34 million loss.

Other master manipulators

Those company managers who wish to engage in "creative
bookkeeping" need not go to the conglomerates for their financial
lessons. Indeed, some of the country's largest and most prestigious
firms manage to stretch the "generally accepted" principles of
accounting.

The classic case of stretching accounting methods concerned the
Ethyl Corporation sale of about ten years ago. In this deal, the

tiny Albermarle Paper Manufacturing Company put together a package to acquire far-larger Ethyl from its two joint owners, Standard Oil of New Jersey and General Motors. Each of these giants owned 50 percent of Ethyl's shares, each had held them for 38 years, each would net about $40 million on the sale. However, the financial reporting of the deal could not have looked more different.

GM showed the $40 million proceeds as *income* for the year, without deducting a penny of operating expenses. Thus, net earnings were inflated by that amount. Jersey went to the other extreme. It never showed the $40 million on its earnings statement *at all,* not even under "recurring income." On the contrary, it buried its profit back in the "statement of stockholders' equity," a remote section of the financial report that few people bother to read. The contrast between GM and Jersey was spectacular. The two largest industrial corporations in the world came up with radically different treatment of earnings from the same transaction.

The consequences of delaying the inevitable is dramatically demonstrated in the Penn Central disaster, and the extent to which management engaged in accounting manipulation was considered by some people as bordering on fraud. A more charitable statement was made by W. Willard Wirtz, former Labor Secretary and one of four reorganization trustees. Referring to the figures reported in the annual statements of Penn Central, Wirtz called them "dubious allies of the truth."

The pre-bankruptcy management of Penn Central, headed by Saunders, was so desperate to make the income account look better that they resorted to unusual means of accounting. It is estimated, for example, that the $89 million reported loss of 1969 would have been an actual loss of $300 million if normal accounting and operating practices had been followed. The management was so desperate that they tried to make short-run and stop-gap profits by inadequately maintaining track and rolling stock. This had the inevitable effect of reducing the supply of serviceable freight cars.

For years, Lockheed Aircraft had "expensed" most of its research and development expenditures. This was generally the custom in the industry and it reflected sound, conservative management. However, when the company reached near-bankruptcy as a result of its C-5A cost overruns, it suddenly began to capitalize some research and development costs that it formerly had expensed. The result was to make earnings appear much better.

Lockheed's error was not so much in the changing of its accounting method, but in the fact that this action was taken in an apparent attempt to conceal a sorry record from stockholders. Indeed, the Securities and Exchange Commission was asking the question: Why didn't Lockheed tell its stockholders sooner that it was in trouble?

Among the nation's most troubled companies has been the giant General Dynamics. In common with many huge, multi-product companies, GD was suffering from poor earnings as the decade came to a close. However real these poor earnings might have been, the company management managed to turn them into something better. To be specific, a $40 million pre-tax loss in 1969 was reported as a $2.5 million profit on the financial statement. This feat was achieved by changing from the more conservative accelerated depreciation to the straight-line method for its resources group. Moreover, this change was made *retroactive for fourteen years.* The effect was to take $13 million of such depreciation into current income.

What are earnings? The accounting credibility gap

The ordinary investor, and most managers, would take the below statements to be factual, truthful, and representative of a financial statement that was quantitatively correct:

> *"We have examined the consolidated balance sheet of the XYZ Company and its subsidiaries as of December 31, and the related statements of income, retained earnings and capital surplus, and the statement of source and application of funds for the year then ended. Our examination was made in accordance with generally accepted auditing procedures as we consider necessary in the circumstances."*
>
> *"In our opinion, the accompanying consolidated financial statements represent fairly the financial position of the XYZ Company and subsidiaries as of December 31, and the results of their operations for the year then ended, in conformity with generally accepted accounting principles which have been applied on a basis consistent with that of the preceding year."*

These two paragraphs signify that experienced men of the accounting profession have checked the figures and found them sound. If this is so, the question arises: How can the figures be manipulated? And the answer is that there are enough loopholes in accounting that are big enough to drive a load of annual reports through. And the "creative bookkeeper" can take advantage of them—in the short run.

Let's take an actual case—modified to conceal company identity—of how different accounting methods can significantly affect the *bottom line* of the income statement. The company is the same, operating policies are the same, and sales volume is the same; however, net earnings are not the same.

XYZ MANUFACTURING COMPANY
CONSOLIDATED INCOME STATEMENT
(000)

	Method A (Conservative)	Method B (Liberal)
Net Sales	$481,618	$487,849
Cost of Goods Sold	402,575	398,496
Gross Profit	79,043	89,352
Other Operating Income		2,382
	79,043	91,734
Selling, General & Administrative Expense	48,421	52,936
	30,622	38,798
Other Income (Expense):		
Interest Expense	3,621	3,746
Income-Subsidiaries	1,077	
Amortization Goodwill	340	
Miscellaneous	538	458
	3,423	4,205
Net Income Before Taxes	27,198	34,593
State Income Tax	1,276	1,625
Federal Income Tax Deferred		697
Federal Income Tax Current	10,476	12,880
Charges Equivalent to Tax Reductions from:		
Investment Tax Credits	1,550	
Tax Loss Carryovers	1,980	594
	15,282	15,797
NET INCOME	11,916	18,795
EARNINGS PER SHARE	$3.98	$6.28

Most of the differences between Method "A" and Method "B" can be seen from the table below. This checkoff list may furnish a guide to the "creative bookkeeper."

Income Statement Account	A Treatment	B Treatment	(000) Difference
Inventories	Last-in, first-out	First-in, first-out	$2,393
Depreciation	Sum of the year's digits	Straight-line	506
Research Expense	Charged as incurred	Amortized in 3 years	383
Acquisition	Treats as purchased	Treats as pooling of interest	See next three items:
Goodwill from Acquisition	Amortize over 10 years	Does not amortize	340
Acquisition Depreciation	Use "larger" base in purchase	Use "smaller" base in purchase and pooling	128
Acquisition Loss Carryovers		Apply against Federal income tax to extent of pooling of interest	1,386
Taxes on Profits of Subsidiaries	Makes no provision as income is earned	Makes no provision until dividends received	90
Investment Tax Credits	Amortize over useful life of equipment	Credits against current taxes	1,312
Unfunded Pension Costs	Amortize over 18 years	No amortization	100
Retirement Allowance	Accrues and expenses prior to retirement	Does not accrue or expense until paid	240
		TOTAL DIFFERENCE	6,878

The funny money game

Nowhere has the impact of accounting been greater than in the "funny money" game of the late sixties and early seventies. This game was played to the hilt by the go-go conglomerates who rationalized it with Wall Street's favorite word: *synergy*. Pythagoras ("The whole is the sum of its parts") was out, and Sperry Rand ("One day we lift a log. The next day we shave a face. We're synergistic.") was in.

The opportunities to jazz up the books were fabulous. The over-extended conglomerates didn't buy other companies so much as they did their earnings. This is illustrated by one of the darlings of fad-conscious Wall Street, National Student Marketing Corporation. The stock of NSMC was trading at 100 times earnings; hence an increase of 10 cents in earnings per share would mean a $10 increase in the price of the stock. Therefore, if NSMC could acquire a company with a price/earnings multiple of 20, it could add these earnings to its own and thereby increase the "worth" of the acquired company by five times. The result: the "swingers" on Wall Street would value the acquired earnings as NSMC's own. Indeed, Wall Street went them one better, and gave bonus points for such a strategy. This was the "funny money game."

Most of the conglomerates (IT&T excepted—they paid cash or common stock) took full advantage of the Swinging Sixties in the stock market. NSMC alone made 22 acquisitions in two years and increased its stock price from the initial $6 in April, 1968, to $154 in December, 1969. But the accounting bubble burst, the Dow Jones average cracked, and NSMC's stock tumbled to $3.50.

"Creative bookeeping" eventually comes home to roost.

ACCOUNTING LESSONS TO BE LEARNED

By generally adhering to the following principles, learned from accounting failure of the past, the executive can use accounting for *management*—not *manipulation:*

Use financial statements to inform, not confuse. Although the financial statement is also a public relations tool, its primary purpose is to report the true facts of financial conditions. So keep the stockholder in mind.

Avoid manipulative disease. It is contagious and may lead to an epidemic.

Avoid the "jazz up the stock" syndrome. A high price/earnings ratio must ultimately be sustained with true earnings, and the inevitable day will arrive when earnings must support the stock price.

Be consistent. Use the same practices every time so that results are believable and the company credible.

Never ry for "quickie" earnings by delaying essential maintenance or operations. Remember Penn Central!

Ask the question: Can the "funny money" route to acquisitions really lead to corporate happiness?

Remember—a dollar borrowed from future earnings must be paid back.

Chapter 19

ORGANIZATION: THE STRUCTURE OF THE SIXTIES DOESN'T FIT THE NEEDS OF THE SEVENTIES

"For my money the most difficult decisions
that I've made have been organizational and
personnel decisions."

Fred Borch
—Chairman, General Electric

This comment by GE's Fred Borch fairly reflects the concern about organization and people that is shown by most of the nation's top managers. In almost any successful company, you will find that it is the principal occupation of the chief executive.

We will make two arguments in this chapter. The first of these is that classical organization theory is still a pretty good foundation upon which to build an organization structure—provided the rigidity of the past is dropped and more attention is paid to the human equation.

The second argument is that organizational fads should be carefully examined before committing company resources to them. Remember the conglomerate idea? Its proponents had hailed it as the corporate archetype of the next half century, "the quintessence of modern management," as Walter Kidde's president, Franc Ricciardi, called it. "Free-form management" was the fad of the sixties. Nicholas Salgo of troubled Bangor Punta predicted that by 1980 there would be only 200 major industrial companies in the U.S., and all would be conglomerates. Now, where is the movement today? Defunct!

What is organization? First, it is a composite of those functions (strategy, planning, control, overall management) that make the company go. However, it is more. For our purposes in this chapter we are concerned more with *structure—communications—*and *people;* how well the organization is structured so that communication is enhanced and how a climate is set for the motivation of people to achieve productivity.

This view of organization can be illustrated by the near failure of another conglomerate, Henry Figge's Automatic Sprinkler (now A.T.O.). Like many of its imitators, the company grew at an accelerated pace and acquired many unrelated operations in the process. These acquisitions were merely "thrown into the pot" without too much regard for monitoring them or for communicating with them. Delegation by profit center was tried and didn't work. Mounting problems went unnoticed due to lack of control. Figge's span of control became too wide and he was unable to spread himself that thin. Communications broke down for lack of a structure to facilitate it. People became frustrated and lethargic. Result: near failure! Reason: bad organization!

Need for organizational change

Nowhere do we find the need for organizational change more apparent than in the critical area concerned with people. The original Henry Ford summarized his view of the people problem with the comment, "The average man won't really do a day's work unless he is caught and can't get out of it." The entire corporate philosophy of the American Telephone and Telegraph Company (AT&T) for the past fifty years has been (and apparently still remains) "provide your employees with security and their loyalty will guarantee service with a smile." The paternalistic, autocratic approach reflected in these comments may have been all right for the great depression, but we are now in the seventies and preparing for the eighties. Something better is required.

General Electric, for years everyone's choice for "best managed company," almost succumbed to bureaucratization disease. At a time when they were trying to revitalize the company with new, young managerial blood, many of the younger go-go types refused to work for the huge, superstructured company because of the molasses-like bureaucracy and snail-like pace in getting ahead. This was reflected in their management trainee program. The security-conscious nuts-and-bolts types were retained, but the aggressive, entrepreneurial types were turned off by the structured organization where they were treated like greenhorns by the many authoritarian managers who had also succumbed to the bureaucracy. Chairman Borch admitted that their enormous losses in computers, jet engineers, and nuclear power were directly attributed to the failure to organize for success. The albatross of yesterday's structure had significantly retarded initiative.

Robert Brooker, the recently retired chief executive of Montgomery Ward and the man who began an urgently needed turnaround in the company's operations, remarked: "In general the most important decisions (of the chief executive) are about people." It might be interesting to note that this view was somewhat different from the one held by the autocratic management that preceded Brooker—a management, incidentally, that had taken Ward's to a seriously ailing position where it was not a contender in most major merchandise markets.

Take the case of General Motors and the need for organizational change. Due somewhat to the influence of Alfred P. Sloan, GM has been for years the "organization man's organization" and the example cited by the business profession when they discuss that topic. The company is not only in the forefront of change, it *causes* change. This is presently happening in their attitude toward the work force—*people.*

Many of GM's managers believe that recapturing the interest of their workers—or at least getting them to tolerate life on the assembly line—is one of the crucial problems of the decade. The general manager of the Cadillac Division summarized this view: "A new breed has been coming into the work force with different ideas and we have to adjust to these new thought patterns." New and better methods, experiments, and organizational innovations are being tried to better accommodate people at all levels. And most important—the chief executive of the company sees his job in terms of his responsibility to stay on top of *organizational change.* This means the accommodation of company structure and policy to the needs of people, both within and without the corporation. And yet, even General Motors missed the boat at their Lordstown, Ohio plant. The management failed to understand the new young workers and productivity sank to unheard of low levels.

The new breed of manager

If we can agree—as we must—that the organization's future success is a direct function of its management, then it is essential to build today for good management tomorrow. This means that we should examine the younger manager, the so-called *new breed.* What makes him tick? What motivates him? How can we facilitate his development so that he will be a leader of tomorrow?

Who is this "new breed" of young manager that belongs to the "accelerated generation." He is clearly something different from his predecessors, the *Organization Man* of the 1950's and the *Young Executive* of the 1960's. Both of these latter types have been the subject of a great deal of speculation in the past two decades, and both have since taken their place in the management ranks of American business and done well. Many are today's leaders.

The Organization Man of the fifties was a paradox; he was reconciled to the fact that he must operate within the organizational imperfections of the company he chose to work for. He was also willing to go along with management toward whatever goals such management judged, in their opinion, to be valid. It is therefore easy to see how his determination to preserve his individuality came in conflict with company goals. He usually compromised in favor of the company. Indeed, the company fulfilled the role of "big daddy."

Then came the Young Executive of the sixties. He was colder and more pragmatic, with a more detached and professional air about him. He was more accountant than manager, more salesman than company man, more inclined to owe his allegiance to his profession than to the company. He was mobile. Although the Young Executive became absorbed in his company, he saw the company as a laboratory in which he could practice his problem-solving skills. Absorbed in his company to the exclusion of almost everything else, he nevertheless had no interest in changing corporate life or corporate goals, and he never doubted the importance of his role.

Now we have the New Breed of the seventies, and he is quite something else. This young man reflects the almost passionate concerns of youth in the 1970's—concerns that largely go unappreciated by the "over thirty" crowd. These concerns include individuality, openness, concern for social environment, humanism, and change. Moreover, the New Breed is determined to be heard. Not only do they decry the dehumanizing environment of American business, but they demand that their companies become involved—with pollution, ecology, racial discrimination, and other social issues of the day. While admitting, and reluctantly accepting, the profit motive in business, the New Breed believes that it is not necessary to maximize it. Their argument is that the American corporation can sustain its corporate longevity, and profit, by defraying all costs which it incurs; this means social as well as economic costs.

But you ask—what about the stockholders? Haven't they a right to press their claim for profit maximization? And the New Breed of managers answers yes—and no. On the one hand, business can argue that by maximizing profits it serves both the stockholders and society best. Moreover, business can argue logically that if it assumes "social" costs voluntarily, while a competitor does not, they can go broke. On the other hand, the New Breed argues, some portion of profits must be assigned to the common good. Isn't the common good the sum of all individual and all corporate goals?

Whatever the answer to the paradox, the executive of the seventies must wrestle with it. Additionally, he cannot ignore or pay lip service to the demands of the New Breed of manager because he is the top management of tomorrow.

Down the classical organization and theory "X"?

Ex-Avis chief, Robert Townsend, suggests in his book, *Up the Organization,* that organization charts "strangle profits and stifle people" and should be chucked altogether.

The president of a large multiproduct firm says, "Take five separate product divisions, try to sell three of the five products to one market segment—say manufacturing. When you do that, conventional organization charting isn't worth a cent."

In his book, *The Peter Principle,* Lawrence Peter makes the argument that the organization chart is partly responsible for the fact that managers tend to rise to their level of incompetence in an organization, and then stay there.

Does this mean that classical organization structure (and the theory "X" manager) is on the way out? The answer is: *not necessarily*. General Motors, IBM, DuPont, Ford, GE, and Chrysler are among those that still operate in a classical way. However, these firms make the necessary modifications, or innovations, to classical structure in order to accommodate change.

What is classical organization?

The four basic pillars that support classical organization theory are these:

> *Specialization of labor*—tasks should be grouped homo-geneously—salesmen in sales, accountants in accounting, engineers in engineering, and so on. (Where do you put computers or government relations?)
>
> *Chain of command*—all authority rests at the top of the organizational pyramid except for those things specifically delegated to lower levels. (The old Army game.)
>
> *Unity of Command*—nobody works for more than one boss.
>
> *Span of Control*—there is a limit (as yet undetermined) to the number of subordinates a manager can supervise. (President Nixon supervises over sixty.)

The classical organization is characterized by *structure—structure—structure*. It is ruled by procedure and directives and has a chart (along with position descriptions) showing who are the order-givers and who are the order-takers.

The very character of the classical organization—structure—structure—structure—is the reason why modern organizational theorists say that it won't work. Humans don't want structure, procedure, close control, direct supervision, standards of performance—the very things that characterize the classical organization. They inhibit productivity.

Despite the fact that classical organization is in disfavor with many academicians and theoreticians, a number of structural modifications are in vogue today. These include the *matrix* (vertical authority through a horizontal structure), *collegial* (sharing the office of the president much as Pan Am has done), *project management* (people are assigned to a project or task force manager and return to their functional spots when the project is complete), *the ladder* (so called because staff experts are located vertically rather than horizontally below the president), *the beehive* (charted in concentric rings like a beehive with over-lapping lines designed to show improved communications). Whatever the form of the organization, it is a take-off on the classical.

What is a theory "X" manager?

By and large, the theory "X" manager is the one who believes in the classical organization structure and the assumption that people will perform as instructed. He believes that if organizational goals are established, tasks defined, and job structured, then those employees who don't perform as directed are pathological. In general, he is convinced that the average worker is somewhat lazy, that he has little appreciation for management's goals (pro-ductivity), and that he desires close supervision, having little innovative spirit of his own. Moreover, if productivity is to be gained from the average employee, sanctions (threats, rewards, fringe benefits) must be applied.

Chrysler: A case of why classical theory must be modified

Classical theory is simple, it is understood by manager and subordinate alike, and by and large, it has worked pretty well. However, it should be modified to fit the needs of the company— and the people—of the seventies. This is demonstrated by the case of Chrysler, and their insistence on following classical principles.

> In 1961, Lynn Townsend took charge of a company knee-deep in troubles. Using a classical organization structure and a personal philosophy of Theory "X" management, Townsend restored its honor, improved its cars, revamped the dealer system, and almost doubled its share of the market. However, as the 1960's drew to a close, Chrysler was in trouble. Part of the reason

was economic conditions, but most of it was due to the company's organizational methods.

Structure: the company was inflexible, both in the market place and in its own organization. The production system was rigid and computerized, and permitted no changes to respond to changing conditions. Line and staff management couldn't communicate. Why should they? Jobs were so structured that people wouldn't risk the consequences of departing from their position descriptions. Both Townsend and his chief subordinate were former accountants, and they forgot momentarily that the name of the game was *selling.*

Controls: Tight operational controls are okay, unless you relax your grip, and none were tighter than those installed by Townsend. However, when these controls slackened, almost overnight Chrysler's profits plummeted and many of the gains that Townsend had labored for years to achieve were obliterated. When controls—and quantitative standards of performance—become the only measure of how a job is done, people become bored and relax at the first opportunity.

Theory "X" Management: Townsend was the classical case of the classical manager. His autocratic style was identified by one top management insider who complained, "Townsend got so damned cocky. It goes to show you, an executive gets into trouble when he starts thinking he's good." Despite everyone's agreement that Chrysler's line of big cars wouldn't sell (one director said "Our big cars are turkeys"), Townsend insisted that "styling was excellent" and refused to go along with restyling and marketing actions that were obvious. When near disaster struck in 1970-71, he tried to repeat his sweeping managerial overhaul by transferring almost every executive in the company, an action hardly expected to improve morale or productivity. Townsend had a case of the "Messiah complex."

Corporate image: When you're hot you're hot

On the wall of the chairman's office at Xerox there formerly hung a framed letter from an irate customer. It was received as a result of the company's widely publicized decision in 1965 to spend $4 million (its entire TV advertising budget) to underwrite a documentary film celebrating the 25th anniversary of the United Nations. The letter says, simply: "You are a bunch of communists. I will never buy your anti-freeze again!" How's that for image?

Is corporate image important to insiders? Compare Vince Lombardi's philosophy, "The only thing that counts is winning," to that of the Buffalo Bill's coach, "We play them one at a time." Compare A&P's motto, "Where economy rules," to that of the gung-ho Melville Shoe Company, "We don't sell shoes, we sell excitement." Which organization is a better one to work for?

To say that image is important is to state an obvious fact. It is important to motivate the customers to buy and to motivate the employees as well. A basic part of the growth strategy of Xerox is to build an image that motivates employees to contribute to such growth. Elements of that strategy include:

(1) emphasis on competence in R&D, marketing skill, and planning ability;
(2) a progressive attitude in which risk is encouraged and loyalty is obtained through high morale;
(3) a go-go attitude; and
(4) an attitudinal environment to support growth.

Can you describe the products or services of TRW? Of Boise Cascade? Of Transamerica? It's a good bet that the ordinary citizen (or customer) cannot. These companies face the problem of image building—both for outsiders and inside employees as well.

The point to remember is this: most companies spend too much money and attention in building their image with outsiders. Perhaps they should devote a little more time to building an organizational image for employees. Otherwise, they might find themselves in the unfortunate position of Consolidated Edison or AT&T. These two firms have a bad image inside as well as outside. Inertia is hard to overcome if ignored too long. It took Eastern Airlines ten years to rid itself of its poor service image.

Line vs. staff

Not too many years ago, when production workers outnumbered white collar workers 9 to 1, there was never any doubt who was in charge. It was *line!* Now the black and white distinction between line and staff is fading into grey as production is automated and shop workers move into the office. The industrial engineer is now the systems analyst. Staff now outnumber line. Service industries make up over half of the GNP.

Despite what has become a disturbing trend for some old-line managers, the trend promises to continue and it raises some potentially troublesome questions. Consider the following representative events:

> Penn Central cuts its number of vice-presidents from 35 to 11.
> Pan Am appoints over 30 vice-presidents in one year.
> American Standard almost loses the market for fiberglass plumbing fixtures because, as one vice-president explained, "We were caught short and we had to move like lightning. The reason was that nobody could be found to make a decision. Each succeeding layer of management had to be continually appraised, but no one had enough authority to make a decision."

After Jim Ling's takeover of Jones and Laughlin Steel, one director recalled that the company "acted like no one owned it." The president said, "We would like to see an organization with people in it who know what their job is." Subsequently, the president fired 20 percent of salaried employees and reduced the number of executives reporting to him from 14 to 7.

These examples are illustrative of a growing dichotomy forced by chief executives. On the one hand, there is need for specialized skills to cope with the increasing complexity of problems confronting headquarters. On the other hand, a lot of deadwood in the executive suite is sure to burden a company. "Over-organization," another term for a lot of staff people, is sure to result in too much fat. This in turn gives you slow decision making, reduced incentive for innovation, and the other results associated with top-heavy staff. And, if you think that staff and fat are not synonymous, ask yourself the question: Whose jobs are the first to be eliminated in times of trouble?

What is the answer? Perhaps it lies in decentralization.

Centralization vs. decentralization

Alfred Sloan of General Motors started it and General Electric, in the late fifties, gave impetus to the decentralization movement. It became a fad. Then, in the sixties, the computer became prevalent. This reporting tool that facilitated central control, plus some spectacular cases of companies that lost control through decentralization (e. g., General Dynamics), set the stage for a re-examination of the merits of decentralization. This examination is still going on.

Let's look at some pros and some cons on the argument:

Pro—Arguments for: Decentralization builds management depth and releases untapped potential and innovation at lower levels. Close supervision inhibits productivity. Nowhere has this been more evident than in the retailing industry. The classical approach in this industry has been to maintain central purchasing, tight procedures, and reduce the store manager to little more than a stock man. Sears, Kresge's, and Penney's are among those who have substantially improved profitability and growth by a policy of decentralization and delegation. A&P has been the antithesis. Decentralization also reduces executive deadwood and the need for a lot of staff people. Litton Industries maintained a very small headquarters staff that supervised over 250 profit centers. This would have been impossible without decentralization.

Rigor mortis is likely to set in at a superstructured staff level. As one executive of U.S. Industries concluded, "One go-go type can do twice the work and assume twice the responsibility of a manager who is stuck in a large superstructure."

Con—Arguments against: There is the need for synergism in the modern complex organization. Together, managers can achieve more than the sum of their efforts individually. Centralization provides synergy.

Decentralization promotes fat. If left alone, the autonomous division manager will build a division staff that rivals headquarters staff. The end result is not reduction of staff, but duplication of staff.

Control is lost through decentralization. The most spectacular case for this argument has been the conglomerates. They grew so fast and in such diverse directions that control was lost. They paid lip service to decentralization because they *had* to delegate. However, the profit center managers did not perform as they had prior to the "shotgun wedding" with the conglomerator.

DuPont provides an example of how one company is wrestling with the problem. Despite the fact that there are cobwebs in the structure of this giant blue chip, and notwithstanding some serious leveling out of recent operating results, DuPont shows signs of regaining its former reputation as one of the world's best-managed firms.

For years, DuPont operated under an advanced system of delegation to twelve general managers of product divisions. Control was maintained by their world famous system of financial reporting. At the top, they had their now questionable "management-by-committee" system, whereby senior vice-presidents (mostly former division managers) acted as committees of consultants. It was said that DuPont's vice-presidents gave orders to no one but their secretaries.

In 1972, DuPont embarked on a plan of fundamental organizational changes. At one extreme they pushed delegation down several levels below division managers into an increased number of profit centers. At the other extreme, they gave their senior vice-presidents line authority over the divisions. Results of this "compromise decentralization" are not available at this writing.

The room at the top

We have examined (in Chapter 14) the role of the president, or chief executive, and made the argument that one-man rule should be avoided. We will end this chapter by considering again the man at the top, and how his managerial ability, or lack of it, can affect the organization. In many ways the top man *is* the organization, in the sense that he provides the leadership and influences the entire company structure.

It has been said by many that the application of the behaviorial sciences is in the stone age. Nevertheless, the chief executive must be a behavioral scientist and know when—and when not—to apply proven behavioral principles of leadership. We can cite a number of cases where this has been done in something less than an optimum way. Most of these involve the "messiah" complex of the top man and his belief that his way is the only way.

General Dynamics was pushed to the brink a number of times by the constant bickering of stockholder Henry Crown and a number of chief executives. These battles at the top left little time or effort for planning and control of the company's operations, and the climate pervaded all levels. David Sarnoff of RCA hung on a little too long. Although the electronic orientation of Robert and his father, the "General," brought the company to its position of prominence, his guidance was not sufficient when the company's diversification program took it outside that area. Chairman Borch of GE admitted that their $500 million loss on the high technology gamble was a result of not organizing for the effort. Jones and Laughlin Steel was paralyzed and teetered on the brink after a takeover by LTV. "Bunkie" Knudsen was enormously successful at General Motors, but didn't have what it took to transfer his charisma to Ford.

Examples of outstanding *success* by the top man are harder to come by.

The position of chief executive is a lonely one, but an exceedingly important one. No one man can run today's complex company in the classical two-fisted style of the past. Whether large or small, today's organization is faced with complexity—in size, markets, technology, internal environment, and the ever-prevailing rapidity of change.

The top executive should communicate freely, consult frequently, but avoid excessive participation and attempts at consensus. Whom to consult is another important question. In many top management meetings, important officers of the corporation, generalists by their position, express many views and opinions of a highly specialized nature. The modern industrial leader who is going to succeed the classical gunslinger will have another characteristic. He will surround himself by the best specialists money and incentives can buy: not personality boys, but experts in various fields comprising his business. He will give them assignments, listen to their answers and analysis, and will then synthesize an opinion and a decision. It will be his decision, and it will have to be implemented by his *operating* team.

He will not trust anybody that will casually report that the implementation is in progress. He'll demand an elaborate, double or triple cross-checking system to know at all times the progress of any key program and its actual results as against anticipation. He will control, control and control to avoid the billion-dollar mistakes of Penn Central, Lockheed, Rolls Royce, General Dynamics, RCA, and so many other "well managed" giants.

As the organization grows, he will have to delegate a great deal of authority. He will select the best team he can, but delegation does not mean abdication. Decentralization and delegation are the two most misunderstood, misused and costly terms in American business. Because of sudden sensitivities, probably brought about by the many psychologists writing on how people feel or don't feel, top executives feel guilty if they check on the progress of their "trusted and competent" associates. The reins loosen, operations become sloppy, and overnight, large losses may appear where there were large profits just a short time ago. The chief executive has not only the right, but the obligation to continuously check and control the performance of his company and his executives. That same spirit and philosophy should be carried all the way down through the ranks to the lowest level employee—blue or white collar.

Thus, really, the classical organization structure of a corporation is not at an end. It is being modified by the times. At the smaller scale of the corporate spectrum, we will need a risk-taking, innovative entrepreneur who pays a lot of attention to the human element, not because he likes it, but because he needs to. At the larger scale of the spectrum, we need a one-man combination of symphony director and controller—a man who selects good players, keeps them in harmony, checks on their performance often, and also calls the tune to be played.

ORGANIZATIONAL DECISIONS: LESSONS TO BE LEARNED

Organization theory and practice is the least structured and most debatable discipline in the study of management. The behavioral sciences, in particular, are difficult to understand and more difficult to apply. Nevertheless, certain fundamental truths appear evident from reviewing successes and failures of the recent past.

Avoid organizational rigor mortis. Change is inevitable and the organization—and its people—must accommodate change.

Organization and people decisions are the most important in the firm. Therefore, they should be the primary concern of the chief executive.

Don't write off the New Breed of manager. He is the leader of tomorrow; as companies assimilated the Organization Man of the Fifties and the Young Executive of the Sixties, they must adapt to the "New Breed" of the Seventies.

Don't be a Theory "X" manager. The days of the autocrat are numbered, if not already gone.

Pay as much attention to your inside image as you do your outside one. What your employees think of the company—your attitudinal strategy—is an essential motivational device.

Be careful of corporate deadwood. Ask yourself: Are all these fat cats in staff really necessary?

Adopt a policy of decentralization. But watch out for its dangers. Shoot for that delicate balance between autonomy and control.

The chief executive must set the organizational climate. Despite all you hear about participative management, the chief executive still casts a long shadow. Teach by example.

Part III
Check Your Own Performance

Chapter 20

HANDICAP YOUR
COMPANY'S MANAGEMENT

"Management is the most important activity
in our society."
—Peter Drucker—

There are dozens of surveys available from such sources as
Fortune and *Forbes* that analyze the comparative performance of
American companies. You can, for example, compare your company with others by size of assets, sales, net income, cash flow,
market value, number of employees, and how your ranking or
position on such lists changes over time. However, if we agree—as
we must—that your performance over time reflects your company's management, then these rankings have a serious shortcoming—they do not tell us how well the company is managed. We
know of no list of 500 best-managed U.S. corporations.

It is not surprising that no such ranking exists. First, there is the
matter of *qualification*. While we can measure and quantify such
items as assets and sales rather easily, what do we do about
assigning a number to a company's leadership climate—or strategy—or organization? Second, since *measures of management*—or
mismanagement—are so ill-defined and affected by so many
variables, few people are willing to attempt the task of relative or
absolute ranking. While we might be able to say the Union Pacific
has been better managed than Penn Central, who can say that IBM
is ahead of Xerox? So the problem remains—how do we measure

that organizational attribute that overshadows all others in importance—good management?

To assist in this problem of ranking your company's top management, we have devised a "do it yourself" system, whereby you play a game of "management golf" with known players (companies). By scoring yourself honestly (no "gimmes" on the short putts), you can arrive at a handicap for your company and compare your score against the hackers, the par shooters, and the occasional sub-par player.

The course

The scorecard is shown in Figure 20-1. The course has eighteen holes, five hazards. Par is a score of 72. If you don't like our holes, you may build some of your own. However, there is a caution— managers like those holes that they find easiest to play. Incidentally, hole #1 is the toughest on the course, and if you cannot get at least a double bogey on this one, it might hurt your game badly for the remaining seventeen holes.

Shooting par on the 18 holes of management

The eighteen holes comprising the course are identified on the left. What it takes to shoot par is described at the right.

DESCRIPTION OF PAR

#1 Strategy (See Chapter 10)

Provide a unified sense of direction to which all members of the organization can relate. A philosophy of management—a corporate course of action—and the objectives and plans to achieve them. Basic ingredient of a "competitive edge." Here are four rules for strategy:

(1) It must be clearly and specifically stated.

(2) It must be agreed upon by all as a way of corporate life.

(3) It must be compatible with the resources of the firm.

SCORE CARD

	Strategy	Operational Planning	Profit Planning	Creative Planning	Marketing	Overall Bookkeeping	Cost Controls	Hardening of Arteries	Mgt. Info. Systems	Board of Directors	Balance	Conglomeration	Management Depth	Organization Structure	Employee Progress	One Man Rule	Innovation	Leadership	React to Change	Capital Structure	Customer Relations	Acc'tg. Practices	Computers	Total (Par = 72)	
HOLE NUMBER	1	2	3	*	4	5	6	*	7	8	9	*	10	11	12	*	13	14	15	*	16	17	18		
PAR	5	4	4	Penalty	5	5	4	Penalty	3	4	3	Penalty	3	5	3	Penalty	4	5	3	Penalty	5	4	3	72	SCORE
QUITTERS																									
Penn Central	8	7	6	3	8	8	8	3	6	6	5	3	4	8	5	1	7	7	5	3	8	8	8	135	
Rolls Royce	8	7	6		7	8	7	1	6	6	4		4	7	4	1	5	6	4	3	6	6	6	112	
Lockheed	7	6	6	2	6	8	8	1	4	6	4		4	6	4		5	6	4	3	6	6	5	107	
HACKERS																									
Pan Am	7	6	6		7	7	6	1	4	6	5		5	7	5	2	5	7	4	1	8	5	4	108	
Ling Temco Vaught	8	7	5	3	7	7	6	1	5	6	4	3	5	7	5	2	5	6	4	3	6	8	4	117	
General Dynamics	7	6	5	1	7	7	7	1	5	5	4	2	4	6	4		5	7	4	2	6	5	4	104	
BOGIE SHOOTERS																									
Chrysler	7	5	5		6	6	5	1	4	5	4		4	6	4	1	5	6	4	1	6	5	5	95	
AT&T	6	5	4		5	5	4	2	3	4	4		3	5	3		5	6	4		8	4	3	83	
A&P	6	5	5		7	6	4	2	4	5	4		5	5	5	1	6	6	4		7	4	4	95	
PAR SHOOTERS																									
Penney's	5	4	4		4	5	4		3	4	3		3	5	3		4	5	3		4	4	3	70	
Walt Disney	4	4	4		5	5	4		3	4	3		3	5	3		4	5	3		5	4	3	71	
General Motors	4	4	5		5	6	4		3	4	3		3	5	3		4	5	3		6	4	3	74	
THE PROS																									
IT&T	4	4	3		5	5	3		3	4	3	1	2	5	3	1	3	4	3		5	4	3	68	
Xerox	4	4	4		4	5	4		3	4	3	1	3	5	3		3	4	3		5	4	3	69	
IBM	4	4	4		4	5	4		3	4	3		3	5	3		4	5	3		4	4	3	69	
Your Competitor																									
Your Company																									

Figure 20-1

	(4) It must be attuned to the corporate environment.
#2 Operational Planning (See Chapter 11)	Develop the necessary *tactical* or *operational* plan for achieving a strategic objective. This involves the classic steps of setting objectives, preparing a work plan, and implementing and controlling progress.
#3 Profit Planning (See Chapter 12)	Determine the operational details of how the *return on investment* objective is to be achieved. The end result is a financial plan that contains objectives and controls for each determinant of profit (e.g., sales, labor, manufacturing expense, distribution, turnover, etc.). Plan your profits *before* and not *after* the fact. Next year's income statement is the model for the profit plan—not last year's. Earnings per share, not sales, is the goal.
#4 Marketing (See Chapter 10)	Develop a marketing strategy to differentiate your product/service and give you a competitive edge. Organize to implement this strategy.
#5 Overall Controls (See Chapter 12)	Develop a management audit, or other method, to insure overall control of major components of the business such as objectives, policies, major functional areas, and external interface. Make sure the subsystems of the organization integrate into a system. CAUTION: Almost all companies have controls over major functions and programs. But watch out! Many of them eitner pay lip service to controls or receive feedback after it's too late to do anything about it.
#6 Cost Controls (See Chapter 12)	Maintain quick feedback through reports that compare performance against a predetermined standard so that any deviations of cost (and time) can be corrected before serious overruns occur.

#7 Management Information Systems (See Chapter 17)	Demand management participation in the design of computer-based systems that serve the decision-making needs of managers—not the needs of the computer technician.
#8 Board of Directors (See Chapter 13)	Make sure that boards are something more than "corporate window dressing." They must participate in management and perform their trustee function—not become a "rubber stamp" for the chief executive.
#9 Organization Balance (See Chapter 19)	Achieve balance between the generalist and the specialist—between the creative and the technical forces—between operations, marketing, and finance. Don't let one function (sales, engineering, finance) achieve disproportionate leverage because of executive interest or experience.
#10 Management Depth (See Chapter 19)	Provide for bench strength in management—both in numbers and quality. Develop your own management strength and don't pirate it from others.
#11 Organization Structure (See Chapter 19)	Adopt a structure that fits the needs of the company and its people. Although the classical structure is traditional and easy to understand, it very likely needs modification to accommodate accelerating complexity and change.
#12 Employee Development (See Chapter 19)	Provide for the release of that vast reservoir of human potential and productivity that exists among the employees of the organization. Human resources are unquestionably the most important in any firm.
#13 Innovation (See Chapter 15)	Don't be a "Monday morning quarterback" or a "follow-the-leader" company. Be innovative in improving productivity, marketing techniques, new products, and better methods.

#14 Leadership (See Chapters 14 & 19)	Establish a climate where people want to go to work because the organization fulfills their need for challenge, responsibility and recognition. Avoid the classical paternalistic or autocratic form of management.
#15 Reaction to Change (See Chapter 15	Don't wait for change to overtake you. Be aware of it, react to it, even *cause* it. Consumer, social, technological, political, and managerial changes are among those to watch out for. Maintain organizational flexibility to be on top of change.
#16 Customer Relations (See Chapter 16)	Admit that the customer is king—yea the emperor! The age of consumerism is upon us and the attitude of "up the customer" will get you nothing but disaster. Plan for the new and growing power of the consumer and make sure this attitude pervades the entire organization, not just the sales force.
#17 Accounting Practices (See Chapter 18)	Be reasonable, consistent, and honest in accounting—both for internal and external uses. Use accounting as a tool of managerial planning and control rather than a device to fool the public.
#18 Computers	Use, but don't misuse computers. If your systems comprise simply a patchwork approach to automation of paperwork—if you have little more than "islands of mechanization"—give yourself a double bogey on this hole. However, if you have a plan underway for the implementation of a management information system—give yourself a par.

The hazards

As every golfer knows, he cannot always keep his ball in the fairway. A bad shot will put him in the rough, or out-of-bounds. Here are the hazards in our management game of golf. Add 1-3 penalty strokes if you find yourself in a hazard.

NAME	HOW TO GET IN THE HAZARD
Creative Bookkeeping	Engaging in manipulations of the books in an attempt to bamboozle the public. Usually done in the "funny money" type of acquisition, or when in dire need to make the "bottom line" look like something that it is not. *Example:* Penn Central—disqualified.
Hardening of Corporate Arteries	Permitting *rigor mortis* to set in because of complacency, nepotism, apathy, a protected market gained through a monopoly position or patent, or management menopause. Leads to rigidity and bureaucratization. *Example:* A.T.& T. A&P—Penalty: 3 strokes
Conglomeration	Becoming enamoured with pyramidal growth for its own sake without regard for synergistic principle. Results could be completely unreal stock price, misleading earnings and growth figures, and financial brinksmanship. *Example:* Jim Ling of LTV—Still looking for lost ball.
One-Man Rule	Letting strong leader run a one-man show in autocratic fashion without management participation. It can't work in the long run. Complex organizations of the '70s require management depth. *Example:* Lynn Townsend of Chrysler—Hooked ball into rough.
Capital Structure	Allowing yourself to get in a liquidity crisis or becoming so over-burdened with debt that interest payments are difficult to meet. *Example:* Pan Am.

Classification of the players (companies)

Companies can be classified according to the way they have scored in the game of management.

TYPE OF COMPANY MANAGEMENT	DESCRIPTION
Dropout	Can't play the game. Picks up his ball before finishing, or disqualifies during game.
Hacker	Much worse than average, but able to finish game.
Bogey Shooter	Plays a fair game, but doesn't par many holes. Worse than average.
Par Shooter	Plays a par game. Much better than average, but not quite a pro.
The Pro	The best. May shoot a birdie on any hole and an eagle if lucky.

Company illustration

Selected illustrations of how various companies have played the different holes will give you an idea of how to estimate your own company's score. Although some companies shoot a par on some holes and double bogies on others, we can rank them in general terms on their overall game.

Our apologies to any firm that feels that we have given them the wrong score. These have been assigned after watching the performance of a lot of players.

COMPANY	HOLE	ILLUSTRATIVE COMMENT
PENN CENTRAL	Board of Directors	Penn Central's board saw no evil, heard no evil, spoke no evil, while management continued its incredible path to bankruptcy.

	Misuse of Computers	Entire trains and over 500 boxcars were "lost" by incompatible computer systems.
		HAZARD: Creative Bookkeeping Penn Central paid $100 million in dividends while it had a negative cash flow. Management tried to cover up impending doom!
ROLLS ROYCE	Cost Controls	Enormous time and cost overruns in an attempt to handle engine for Lockheed's airbus.
	Operational Planning	Failed to plan properly for growth and diversification into new markets (U.S. aerospace).
LOCKHEED	Profit Planning	Fantastic cost overruns and the resulting disaster is attributable to lack of sound financial planning. MORAL: Don't let engineers do your financial planning and control.
	Innovation	Became "follow-the-leader" defense contractor, putting all eggs in one basket. Depended on Defense Department for Research and Development.
LING TEMCO VOUGHT	Strategy Organization	LTV grew so fast and was so disorganized that there wasn't time for structure, coordination, and there was little communication between parts.

CHRYSLER	Employee Development	Organization was structured and restructured so frequently—with no accompanying management depth—that Chrysler became "just a place to work."
	Strategy	Missed the boat almost completely on foreign markets and small cars. *HAZARD: One-Man Rule.* Chrysler suffered for years under the one-man rule of Lynn Townsend. Finally, what was formerly Townsend's "rubber stamp board" made him get help.
AT&T	Marketing	Over-did the "monopoly" syndrome. The result was that badly lagging service caught up with them.
	Customer Relations	Failed in the delivery of their one product— public service. Now engaged in trying to rebuild public confidence that it took decades to build.
A&P	Reaction to Change	Failed to foresee the major shift of consumer buying to suburban shopping centers. Also failed to act upon shift once it caught up with them.

		HAZARD:: *Hardening of Corporate Arteries.* Both AT&T and A&P suffered from a bad case of this affliction. Much of their pioneering spirit was lost because of the inertia of the past and the bureaucratization of their management.
J.C. PENNEY	Profit Planning	This turn-around company in retailing has not only diversified into other lines (à la Sears), but has shown the industry how to do it at a profit through strict profit planning and control.
WALT DISNEY	Innovation	After segmenting his market long ago and capitalizing on a proven strategy, this movie-maker has continued to innovate in products and services as well as his marketing.
	Customer Relations	While achieving the above growth and profitability, the company has managed to be among the leaders in good will and repeat business.
GENERAL MOTORS	Management Depth	This auto maker is noted as a training ground for managers. In fact, they export talent to Chrysler and many others.

	Leadership Climate	As opposed to Chrysler where it is "just a place to work"—at G.M. it is a "fun place to work."
IT&T	Conglomeration	As opposed to LTV and the majority of the other conglomerates, IT&T, under the leadership of Harold Geneen, has maintained a steady, balanced, *synergistic* growth in size and earnings. Equity capital and not "funny money" financed this growth, a rate that is second only to IBM in earnings per share.
XEROX	Marketing	Xerox took their "go-go" philosophy, combined it with their innovative management, and marketed copiers in a style that was the envy of the business world.
IBM	Reaction to Change	No other firm in history has kept on top of technology and made it *profitable* like IBM. This firm, whose stock has the highest total market value of any firm in the U.S., has played all the holes well—as have our other birdie shooters.

Score your company

Now that you are familiar with the course and the hazards, play the game and compare your company's score with that of our illustrative players. You may also want to compute the score of your competitor.

And remember—hackers can become pros if they do their homework and practice.

LET'S TEE OFF!

ABOUT THE AUTHORS

JOEL ROSS co-authored this book as a result of years of research and teaching in general management, business strategy and policy. He has authored three books and numerous articles on related subjects and is a frequent platform speaker and participant in management development programs. He is currently Director of Graduate Programs in Business at Florida Atlantic University.

MICHAEL J. KAMI, former Corporate Director of Long Range Planning for IBM and Vice President of Corporate Planning for Xerox, was one of the pioneers of the techniques of overall planning in the United States and is considered one of the leading authorities in the field. He has consulted on planning, growth and innovation with businesses both large and small.

DATE DUE

DISPLAY		
Emphasis '82		
MAY 24 '83		
MAY 17 1983		
DE 20 '93		
GAYLORD		PRINTED IN U.S.A.

Let's Pretend
Poems of Flight and Fancy

Let's Pretend

Poems of Flight and Fancy

Compiled by Natalie S. Bober

Pictures by Bill Bell

VIKING KESTREL

ACKNOWLEDGMENTS

For their help along the way, my gratitude to the following people: to Adrienne Betz, who first made me believe that I could do a book of poems; to special friend Estelle Riback who worked closely with me to give the book shape and form, and to make the final critical decisions; to my daughter, Betsy Bober Polivy, who helped in the early search for poems; and to Marci Dressler, who tracked down sources and discovered some special poems.

My son Stephen judged the essay with the critical eye of an English teacher. My daughter-in-law, Patricia Lukens, read the poems aloud to her young friends and to my grand-daughter Lani, and passed on to me their reactions.

But the greatest thanks go to my grand-daughter Jody, who took me back to the Land of Let's Pretend when she was just a little girl, and who listened to all the poems, giving me the benefit of her child's-eye perspective. This is, in truth, her book.   N.S.B.

VIKING KESTREL

Viking Penguin Inc., 40 West 23rd Street, New York, New York 10010, U.S.A.
Penguin Books Ltd, Harmondsworth, Middlesex, England
Penguin Books Australia Ltd, Ringwood, Victoria, Australia
Penguin Books Canada Limited, 2801 John Street, Markham, Ontario, Canada L3R 1B4
Penguin Books (N.Z.) Ltd, 182–190 Wairau Road, Auckland 10, New Zealand

Copyright © Natalie Bober, 1986
Illustration copyright © Bill Bell, 1986
All rights reserved
First published in 1986 by Viking Penguin Inc.
Published simultaneously in Canada
Printed in U.S.A. by Lake Book/Cuneo Inc., Melrose Park, Illinois
Set in Zapf International Medium
1   2   3   4   5   90   89   88   87   86
The following two pages constitute an extension of this copyright page.

LIBRARY OF CONGRESS CATALOGING IN PUBLICATION DATA
Bober, Natalie. Let's pretend.
Summary: A collection of poems using the theme of
imagination, by writers from Robert Louis
Stevenson to Eve Merriam and Shel Silverstein.
1. Imagination—Juvenile poetry.   2. Children's poetry, American.
3. Children's poetry, English. [1. Imagination—Poetry.   2. American poetry—
Collections.   3. English poetry—Collections]   I. Bell, Bill, ill.   II. Title.
PS595.I46B6   1986   811'.008'0353   86-7782   ISBN 0-670-81176-9

for Jody
who took me back to the Land of Let's Pretend
and for Lani and Joelle
who keep me there

INTRODUCTION

The gift of fantasy and the ability to use the imagination are among the greatest gifts of childhood. "Let's Pretend" is the password to the land of magic, an enchanted land inhabited by elves and fairies, animals that talk, objects that miraculously come to life, and sometimes even imaginary playmates.

Children learn through imagination because they can't understand, intellectually, much of what is happening around them. It is only through fanciful images that they can begin to recognize and comprehend their own feelings and experiences.

For children who are attempting to develop a sense of "I," listening to a poem that tells them, "My Inside-Self and My Outside-Self are different as can be," can help crystalize their own thoughts about who they are. And as they dream with other poets about what they might like to be, they can try on different roles.

Young children are primarily interested in themselves. Poems that echo the long-ings, the wishes, the dreams of childhood in the rhythmic beat of its language can sing their way into the child's spirit and set aflame their imagination. Poems that lead children to ponder the perplexing questions that are at the back of their minds but which they cannot express ("Will there really be a morning?") can be a positive, happy way to stretch their hearts as well as their minds.

We know that our imagination can change the way we look at something. By allowing us to use our *minds* to see, it provides a different way of seeing. Poems of the imagination, then, can become vehicles that help children view themselves and the world around them in a new way.

We know, too, that many fears inhabit the small child's world. From the earliest years these fears are part of a child's everyday life. The play of light and shadow in a darkened room at bedtime or the gurgling, banging noise of a radiator when the heat comes on (that sounded to one little girl like "Bumpy, Bumpy Bears") can convince a child that there's something—or someone—lurking in the room. But a poem about Radiator Lions who "love to fight but will not bite" might help to overcome this fear.

Poems that take children to Fantasyland are, for them, a mirror of their inner experiences. They can provide a steadying power, something to hold on to, an anchor in a rough sea. Fantasy, made up of elements that exist only in the imagination, can take children on a journey to an enchanted land from which they can look back at the "real world" through the window of their imagination. Fantasy can help them to see a world that *could* be, a world in which nothing is impossible.

It is the great gift of the imagination, the gift of wonder, that sets human beings apart from all other living creatures. To fantasize, to dream, makes it possible for the child *and* the adult to strive for greater achievement, to make their own magic, to enter the world of "Why Not?" "Let's Pretend" can provide the opportunity for them to explore the environment together, to see what might be, to hope, to dream.

The range of human imagination is limitless. With a little imagination we can be all we want to be. But how can we stretch that imagination? What can we, as parents, grandparents, teachers, friends, do to nourish and develop it?

We can nurture it through poetry, for poetry is the language of childhood. Poetry says the most important things in the simplest way. It has the power to sort out our experiences and give them order and meaning. "A poem is a momentary stay against confusion," the American poet Robert Frost told us. "Each poem clarifies something." It is "a voyage in discovery" that "begins in delight and ends in wisdom."

It is important to remember, though, that young children may enjoy a poem even though they don't fully understand it. Short, simple poems meet children on their own level, but material that is a little more difficult provides something to grow on, to wonder about. Imagination will take children well beyond their limited experience. It will allow them to be enticed by the poet into the world of "Let's Pretend" and to wander freely over the landscape of the poet's imagination. They can make of the poem anything they will. They can make it *their* poem. It can help them to grow emotionally, esthetically, intellectually.

We must remember, too, that poetry cannot be read hurriedly. It cannot be skimmed. One reading is never enough. Each successive reading reveals more of the poem to the child.

At an age when the love of poetry is ready to be born and nurtured, when pleasure can be derived through the sound of words, hearing a poem is the greatest gift a child can receive. For nothing can give the child the gift of himself or herself more simply, more directly, than a poem.

We should remember the English poet William Wordsworth's lines in *The Prelude*. Describing his childhood, he recalled the time

> when first
> My ears began to open to the charm
> Of words in tuneful order, found them sweet
> For *their own sakes*, a passion and a power.

It is through feeling its rhythm and hearing its words and rhyme that children come to enjoy poetry. Our voice can help to clarify—and simplify—its meaning. As we read aloud, being attentive always to content and form, we help tune their ears to the music of poetry. For it is through *sound* that young children find the way to a poem.

So let us heed the call of Walter De la Mare, another poet loved by children, as he tells us:

> Eyes bid ears:
> Hark
> Ears bid eyes
> Mark:
> Mouth bids nose
> Smell:
> Nose says to mouth
> I will:
> Heart bids mind
> Wonder:
> Mind bids heart
> Ponder.

CONTENTS

My Inside-Self : *"I'd like to change places"*   1

Magical People : *"I met a little elf-man once"*   11

Secrets : *"And all the playthings come alive"*   23

MY INSIDE SELF

"I'd like to change places"

MY INSIDE-SELF

My Inside-Self and my Outside-Self
Are different as can be.
My Outside-Self wears gingham smocks,
And very round is she,
With freckles sprinkled on her nose,
And smoothly parted hair,
And clumsy feet that cannot dance
In heavy shoes and square.

But oh, my little Inside-Self—
In gown of misty rose
She dances lighter than a leaf
On blithe and twinkling toes;
Her hair is blowing gold, and if
You chanced her face to see,
You would not think she could belong
To staid and sober me!

Rachel Field

CHANGING

I know what I feel like;
I'd like to be *you*
And feel what *you* feel like.
And do what *you* do.
I'd like to change places
For maybe a week
And look like your look-like
And speak as you speak
And think what you're thinking
And go where you go
And feel what you're feeling
And know what you know.
I wish we could do it;
What fun it would be
If I could try you out
And you could try me.

Mary Ann Hoberman

DREAM VARIATION

To fling my arms wide
In some place of the sun,
To whirl and to dance
Till the white day is done.
Then rest at cool evening
Beneath a cool tree
While night comes on gently,
   Dark like me—
That is my dream!

To fling my arms wide
In the face of the sun,
Dance! Whirl! Whirl!
Till the quick day is done.
Rest at pale evening . . .
A tall, slim tree . . .
Night coming tenderly
   Black like me.

Langston Hughes

THE SIDEWALK RACER
or
ON THE SKATEBOARD

Skimming
an asphalt sea
I swerve, I curve, I
sway; I speed to whirring
sound an inch above the
ground; I'm the sailor
and the sail, I'm the
driver and the wheel.
I'm the one and only
single engine
human auto
mobile.

Lillian Morrison

I'D LIKE TO BE A LIGHTHOUSE

I'd like to be a lighthouse
   All scrubbed and painted white.
I'd like to be a lighthouse
   And stay awake all night
To keep my eye on everything
   That sails my patch of sea;
I'd like to be a lighthouse
   With the ships all watching me.

                     Rachel Field

AMBITION

If I were a rocket
Shot high across the night,
I'd rather burst in silver stars
Than green or purple light;

For then, perhaps, I'd fool the moon,
Although she's very wise,
And thinking me a baby star
She'd keep me in the skies.

                     John Farrar

A SONG OF GREATNESS

When I hear the old men
Telling of heroes,
Telling of great deeds
Of ancient days,
When I hear them telling,
Then I think within me
I too am one of these.

When I hear the people
Praising great ones,
Then I know that I too
Shall be esteemed,
I too when my time comes
Shall do mightily.

A Chippewa Indian song
(transcribed by
Mary Austin)

THE QUESTION

People always say to me
"What do you think you'd like to be
When you grow up?"
And I say "Why,
I think I'd like to be the sky
Or be a plane or train or mouse
Or maybe be a haunted house
Or something furry, rough and wild . . .
Or maybe I will stay a child."

Karla Kuskin

MAGICAL PEOPLE

"I met a little elf-man once"

THE LITTLE ELF

I met a little elf-man once,
  Down where the lilies blow.
I asked him why he was so small,
  And why he didn't grow.

He slightly frowned, and with his eye
  He looked me through and through.
"I'm quite as big for me," said he,
"As you are big for you."

John Kendrick Bangs

ELVES AND APPLE TREES

Elves love best of all to run
Through old orchards in the sun,
By gnarled and twisted apple trees
With crooked arms and knobbly knees,
With roots like humps, and leaves like hair,
And twigs that clutch and claw the air.
They help to hang the blossoms out
And in the fall, oh, never doubt
When apples shine above your head
It was some Elf who made them red!

Rachel Field

THE BUBBLE FAIRY

I blew a bubble
('Twasn't any trouble),
A real soap bubble
  As big as
    That.

And right in the middle
With wings all a-twiddle,
Sat an elf with a fiddle
  And a bright pink
    Hat.

He tidied his clothes and
He jiggled his toes and
He scratched on his nose and
  He didn't say a
    Thing

But just sort of hung
To the bubble and swung.
Then he stuck out his tongue
  And the bubble went—
    Bing!
           Marjorie Barrows

FAIRY AEROPLANES

The fairies, too, have aeroplanes,
To carry them about,
That swoop, and soar, and dart, and dip,
And circle in and out.

So when their little wings are tired,
They summon one of these,
And sail above the garden beds
Or anywhere they please.

The fairies' aeroplanes are safe
And never do capsize,
They're very beautiful and gay,
Because they're butterflies.

Anne Blackwell Payne

A FAIRY WENT A-MARKETING

A fairy went a-marketing—
  She bought a little fish;
She put it in a crystal bowl
  Upon a golden dish.
An hour she sat in wonderment
  And watched its silver gleam,
And then she gently took it up
  And slipped it in a stream.

A fairy went a-marketing—
  She bought a colored bird;
It sang the sweetest, shrillest song
  That ever she had heard.
She sat beside its painted cage
  And listened half the day,
And then she opened wide the door
  And let it fly away.

A fairy went a-marketing—
  She bought a winter gown
All stitched about with gossamer
  And lined with thistledown.
She wore it all the afternoon
  With prancing and delight,
Then gave it to a little frog
  To keep him warm at night.

A fairy went a-marketing—
  She bought a gentle mouse
To take her tiny messages,
  To keep her tiny house.
All day she kept its busy feet
  Pit-patting to and fro,
And then she kissed its silken ears,
  Thanked it, and let it go.

Rose Fyleman

18

HALLOWE'EN SONG

Three little witches
   Pranced in the garden,
Three little witches
   Danced from the moon;
One wore a wishing hat,
One held a pussy-cat,
One went a pitty-pat
   And whispered a tune.

Out flew an owl
   Who glared at the kitten,
Out flew an owl
   Who stared at the rest,
Dancing, with haughty nose,
Each on the other's toes,
Down past the pumpkin rows
   Under his nest.

Three little witches
   Blew on their broomsticks,
Three little witches
Flew to their queen,
Over the windy glen
Into the night . . . But then
They will be back again
Next Hallowe'en.

Marjorie Barrows

SNOW FAIRIES

I watched a little snowflake
   Come sailing from the sky,
It played a joke on me when
   It fell right in my eye!
Another little snowflake
   Came dancing toward the south,
It looked at me a minute—
   Then landed in my mouth!
They seemed like little fairies
   Upon a holiday,
Just out for fun and frolic
   And asking me to play!

Isla Paschal Richardson

COULD IT HAVE BEEN A SHADOW?

What ran under the rosebush?
   What ran under the stone?
Could it have been a shadow,
   Running away alone?
Maybe a fairy's shadow,
   Slipping away at dawn
To guard a gleaming pot of gold
   For a busy leprechaun.

Monica Shannon

THE PLUMPUPPETS

When little heads weary have gone to their bed,
When all the good nights and the prayers have been said,
Of all the good fairies that send bairns to rest
The little Plumpuppets are those I love best.

If your pillow is lumpy, or hot, thin and flat,
The little Plumpuppets know just what they're at;
They plump up the pillow, all soft, cool and fat—
The little Plumpuppets plump-up it!

The little Plumpuppets are fairies of beds:
They have nothing to do but to watch sleepy heads;
They turn down the sheets and they tuck you in tight,
And they dance on your pillow to wish you good night!

No matter what troubles have bothered the day,
Though your doll broke her arm or the pup ran away;
Though your handies are black with the ink that was spilt—
Plumpuppets are waiting in blankets and quilt.

If your pillow is lumpy, or hot, thin and flat,
The little Plumpuppets know just what they're at;
They plump up the pillow, all soft, cool and fat—
The little Plumpuppets plump-up it!

Christopher Morley

THE CHILD NEXT DOOR

The child next door has a wreath on her hat;
Her afternoon frock sticks out like that,
     All soft and frilly;
She doesn't believe in fairies at all
(She told me over the garden wall)—
She thinks they're silly.

The child next door has a watch of her own;
She has shiny hair and her name is Joan;
     (Mine's only Mary).
But doesn't it seem very sad to you
To think that she never her whole life through
     Has seen a fairy?

Rose Fyleman

SECRETS

"And all the playthings come alive."

BINKER

Binker—what I call him—is a secret of my own,
And Binker is the reason why I never feel alone.
Playing in the nursery, sitting on the stair,
Whatever I am busy at, Binker will be there.

Oh, Daddy is clever, he's a clever sort of man,
And Mummy is the best since the world began,
And Nanny is Nanny, and I call her Nan—
     But they can't
     See
     Binker.

Binker's always talking, 'cos I'm teaching him to
     speak:
He sometimes likes to do it in a funny sort of
     squeak,
And he sometimes likes to do it in a hoodling sort of
     roar . . .
And I have to do it for him 'cos his throat is rather
     sore.

Oh, Daddy is clever, he's a clever sort of man,
And Mummy knows all that anybody can,
And Nanny is Nanny, and I call her Nan—
     But they don't
     Know
     Binker.

Binker's brave as lions when we're running in the
     park;
Binker's brave as tigers when we're lying in the
     dark;

Binker's brave as elephants. He never, never
    cries . . .
Except (like other people) when the soap gets in his
    eyes.

Oh, Daddy is Daddy, he's a Daddy sort of man,
And Mummy is as Mummy as anybody can,
And Nanny is Nanny, and I call her Nan . . .
        But they're not
        Like
        Binker.

Binker isn't greedy, but he does like things to eat,
So I have to say to people when they're giving me a
    sweet,
"Oh, Binker wants a chocolate, so could you give
    me two?"
An then I eat it for him, 'cos his teeth are rather
    new.

Well, I'm very fond of Daddy, but he hasn't time to
    play,
And I'm very fond of Mummy, but she sometimes
    goes away,
And I'm often cross with Nanny when she wants to
    brush my hair . . .

But Binker's always Binker, and is certain to be
    there.

A. A. Milne

MAGIC

Sandra's seen a leprechaun,
Eddie touched a troll,
Laurie danced with witches once,
Charlie found some goblins' gold.
Donald heard a mermaid sing;
Susy spied an elf,
But all the magic I have known
I've had to make myself.

Shel Silverstein

MY SHADOW

I have a little shadow that goes in and out with me,
And what can be the use of him is more than I can see.
He is very, very like me from the heels up to the head;
And I see him jump before me, when I jump into my bed.

The funniest thing about him is the way he likes to grow—
Not at all like proper children, which is always very slow;
For he sometimes shoots up taller like an India-rubber ball,
And he sometimes gets so little that there's none of him at all.

He hasn't got a notion of how children ought to play,
And can only make a fool of me in every sort of way.
He stays so close beside me, he's a coward you can see;
I'd think shame to stick to nursie as that shadow sticks to me!

Robert Louis Stevenson

RADIATOR LIONS

George lives in an apartment and
His mother will not let
Him keep a dog or polliwog
Or rabbit for a pet.

So he has Radiator Lions.
(The parlor is the zoo.)
They love to fight but will not bite
Unless he tells them to.

And days when it is very cold
And he can't go outdoors
They glower and they lower and they
Crouch upon all fours.

And roar most awful roarings and
Gurgle loud and mad.
Up their noses water goeses—
That's what makes them bad.

But he loves Radiator Lions!
He's glad, although they're wild,
He hasn't dogs and polliwogs
Like any other child!

                                Dorothy Aldis

THE RAGGEDY DOLL

The raggedy doll said, "I don't mind
That my dress is held with a pin behind,
Or that the sawdust is out of my toe . . .
'Cause I'm just a raggedy doll, you know."

The raggedy doll said, "I don't care
If you let me sit on the wobbly chair
With my feet up high and my head down low . . .
'Cause I'm just a raggedy doll, you know."

The raggedy doll said, "Really, Nan,
I don't give a fig for a feathery fan
Or a ruffle of lace or a furbelow . . .
'Cause I'm just a raggedy doll, you know."

And Nan took the raggedy doll to bed
And whispered close to her frowzelly head,
"You're awful nice and I love you SO
'Cause you're my raggedy doll, you know,
My very own raggedy doll, you know."

Aileen Fisher

TRAVEL

The railroad track is miles away,
    And the day is loud with voices speaking,
Yet there isn't a train goes by all day
    But I hear its whistle shrieking.

All night there isn't a train goes by,
    Though the night is still for sleep and dreaming,
But I see its cinders red on the sky,
    And hear its engine steaming.

My heart is warm with the friends I make,
    And better friends I'll not be knowing,
Yet there isn't a train I wouldn't take,
    No matter where it's going.

                              Edna St. Vincent Millay

FOREIGN LANDS

Up into the cherry tree
Who should climb but little me?
I held the trunk with both my hands
And looked abroad on foreign lands.

I saw the next door garden lie,
Adorned with flowers before my eye,
And many pleasant places more
That I had never seen before.

I saw the dimpling river pass
And be the sky's blue looking-glass;
The dusty roads go up and down
With people tramping into town.

If I could find a higher tree
Farther and farther I should see,
To where the grown-up river slips
Into the sea among the ships,

To where the roads on either hand
Lead onward into fairy land,
Where all the children dine at five,
And all the playthings come alive.

Robert Louis Stevenson

EVERY TIME I CLIMB A TREE

Every time I climb a tree
Every time I climb a tree
Every time I climb a tree
I scrape a leg
Or skin a knee
And every time I climb a tree
I find some ants
Or dodge a bee
And get the ants
All over me.

And every time I climb a tree
Where have you been?
They say to me
But don't they know that I am free
Every time I climb a tree?
I like it best
To spot a nest
That has an egg
Or maybe three

And then I skin
The other leg
But every time I climb a tree
I see a lot of things to see
Swallows rooftops and TV
And all the fields and farms there be
Every time I climb a tree
Though climbing may be good for ants
It isn't awfully good for pants
But still it's pretty good for me
Every time I climb a tree.

David McCord

32

WOULDN'T YOU?

If I
Could go
As high
And low
As the wind
As the wind
As the wind
Can blow—

I'd go!

John Ciardi

IF PIGS COULD FLY

If pigs could fly, I'd fly a pig
To foreign countries small and big—
   To Italy and Spain,
To Austria, where cowbells ring,
To Germany, where people sing—
   And then come home again.

I'd see the Ganges and the Nile;
I'd visit Madagascar's isle,
   And Persia and Peru.
People would say they'd never seen
So odd, so strange an air-machine
   As that on which I flew.

Why, everyone would raise a shout
To see his trotters and his snout
   Come floating from the sky;
And I would be a famous star
Well known in countries near and far—
   If only pigs could fly!

James Reeves

From: SOMEWHERE

Could you tell me the way to Somewhere—
   *Some*where, *Some*where,
   I have heard of a place called Somewhere—
   But know not where it can be.
     It makes no difference,
     Whether or not
     I go in dreams
     Or trudge on foot:
Would you tell me the way to Somewhere,
   The Somewhere meant for me.

               Walter De la Mare

EEKA, NEEKA

Eeka, Neeka, Leeka, Lee—
Here's a lock without a key;
Bring a lantern, bring a candle,
Here's a door without a handle;
Shine, shine, you old thief Moon,
Here's a door without a room;
Not a whisper, moth or mouse,
Here's a room without a house!

Say nothing, creep away,
And live to knock another day!

               Walter De la Mare

THE SECRET CAVERN

Underneath the boardwalk, way, way back,
There's a splendid cavern, big and black—
If you want to get there, you must crawl
Underneath the posts and steps and all.
When I've finished paddling, there I go—
None of all the other children know!

There I keep my treasures in a box—
Shells and colored glass and queer-shaped rocks,
In a secret hiding place I've made,
Hollowed out with clamshells and a spade,
Marked with yellow pebbles in a row—
None of all the other children know!

It's a place that makes a splendid lair,
Room for chests and weapons and one chair.
In the farthest corner, by the stones,
I shall have a flag with skulls and bones
And a lamp that casts a lurid glow—
None of all the other children know!

Sometime, by and by, when I am grown,
I shall go and live there all alone;
I shall dig and paddle till it's dark,
Then go out and man my private bark:
I shall fill my cave with captive foe—
None of all the other children know!

                              Margaret Widdemer

PAPER BOATS

Day by day I float my paper boats one by one down the running stream.
In big black letters I write my name on them and the name of the village
    where I live.
I hope that someone in some strange land will find them and know who I
    am.
I load my little boats with shiuli flowers from our garden, and hope that
    these blooms of dawn will be carried safely to land in the night.
I launch my paper boats and look up into the sky and see the little clouds
    setting their white bulging sails.
I know not what playmate of mine in the sky sends them down the air to
    race with my boats!
When night comes I bury my face in my arms and dream that my paper
    boats float on and on under the midnight stars.
The fairies of sleep are sailing in them, and the lading is their baskets full of
    dreams.

Rabindranath Tagore

A TASTE OF NATURE

"I'm the one who woke the sun"

VERY EARLY

When I wake in the early mist
The sun has hardly shown
And everything is still asleep
And I'm awake alone.
The stars are faint and flickering.
The sun is new and shy.
And all the world sleeps quietly,
Except the sun and I.
And then beginning noises start,
The whrrrs and huffs and hums,
The birds peep out to find a worm,
The mice squeak out for crumbs,
The calf moos out to find the cow,
And taste the morning air
And everything is wide awake
And running everywhere.
The dew has dried,
The fields are warm,
The day is loud and bright,
And I'm the one who woke the sun
And kissed the stars good night.

Karla Kuskin

THE SUN

I told the Sun that I was glad,
   I'm sure I don't know why;
Somehow the pleasant way he had
   Of shining in the sky,
Just put a notion in my head
   That wouldn't it be fun
If, walking on the hill, I said
   "I'm happy" to the Sun.
                John Drinkwater

I MEANT TO DO MY WORK TO-DAY

I meant to do my work to-day—
   But a brown bird sang in the apple-tree,
And a butterfly flitted across the field,
   And all the leaves were calling me.

And the wind went sighing over the land,
   Tossing the grasses to and fro,
And a rainbow held out its shining hand—
   So what could I do but laugh and go?
                Richard Le Gallienne

CREATION OF FISH, FOWL, AND CATTLE

Be!
Be, caterpillar and comet,
be porcupine and planet,
seas and solar system,
sing with us,
dance with us,
rejoice with us
for the glory of creation,
sea gulls and seraphim,
angel worms and angel host,
chrysanthemum and cherubim
Be!
Sing for the glory
of the living and the loving
the flaming of Creation
sing with us
dance with us
be with us
Be!

Genesis 1:20–25
Madeleine L'Engle

THE LAST WORD OF A BLUEBIRD
As told to a child

As I went out a Crow
In a low voice said, "Oh,
I was looking for you.
How do you do?
I just came to tell you
To tell Lesley (will you?)
That her little Bluebird
Wanted me to bring word
That the north wind last night
That made the stars bright
And made ice on the trough
Almost made him cough
His tail feathers off.
He just had to fly!
But he sent her good-by,
And said to be good,
And wear her red hood,
And look for skunk tracks
In the snow with an ax—
And do everything!
And perhaps in the spring
He would come back and sing."

Robert Frost

SPRING

I'm shouting
I'm singing
I'm swinging through trees
I'm winging sky-high
With the buzzing black bees.
I'm the sun
I'm the moon
I'm the dew on the rose.
I'm a rabbit
Whose habit
Is twitching his nose.
I'm lively
I'm lovely
I'm kicking my heels.
I'm crying "Come dance"
To the freshwater eels.
I'm racing through meadows
Without any coat.
I'm a gamboling lamb
I'm a light leaping goat
I'm a bud
I'm a bloom
I'm a dove on the wing.
I'm running on rooftops
And welcoming spring!

Karla Kuskin

THE TRAGEDY

As I went out a-walking,
   All on a summer's day,
I met a dandelion
   Standing proudly in the way.

But something very dreadful
   Must have happened over night;
When I passed that way next morning,
   His hair had all turned white!

Anne Cooper

THE NIGHT WILL NEVER STAY

The night will never stay,
The night will still go by,
Though with a million stars
You pin it to the sky;
Though you bind it with the blowing wind
And buckle it with the moon,
The night will slip away
Like sorrow or a tune.

Eleanor Farjeon

46

THE WIND

I love the blustering noisy wind
    That blows the boughs on high,
That swirls my hair and tugs my skirts,
    As it goes rushing by.

It rustles in the robins' nests,
    Now here—now there—now by;
I cannot hold it in my hands,
    No matter how I try.

O wind, is it you who carries
    The swallows up so high,
Until they look like small black notes
    Of music on the sky?

            Marion Stauffer Doyle

THE DANCE OF THE LEAVES

"Come on, let's dance," the gay Wind cried,
   "I'll whistle you a song."
Then twirling, whistling, light and free,
   The Brown Leaves swept along.

They danced upon their tiptoes, then
   Turned handsprings in the air,
And dancing, prancing down the street—
   Brown Leaves were everywhere!

They glided on the sidewalks; there
   They'd bounce and pounce and leap,
But when the gay Wind went away—
   The Brown Leaves went to sleep!

               Isla Paschal Richardson

THE MOON'S THE NORTH WIND'S COOKY

The Moon's the North Wind's cooky.
He bites it, day by day,
Until there's but a rim of scraps
That crumble all away.

The South Wind is a baker.
He kneads clouds in his den,
And bakes a crisp new moon that . . . greedy
North . . . Wind . . . eats . . . again!

               Vachel Lindsay

From: ADDRESS TO A CHILD
DURING A BOISTEROUS WINTER EVENING

What way does the wind come? What way does he go?
He rides over the water, and over the snow,
Through wood, and through vale; and o'er rocky height,
Which the goat cannot climb, takes his sounding flight;
He tosses about in every bare tree,
As, if you look up, you plainly may see;
But how he will come, and whither he goes,
There's never a scholar in England knows.

Hark! over the roof he makes a pause,
And growls as if he would fix his claws
Right in the slates, and with a huge rattle
Drive them down, like men in a battle.
But let him rage round; he does us no harm,
We build up the fire, we're snug and warm;
Untouched by his breath, see the candle shines bright,
And burns with a clear and steady light.
Books have we to read—but that half-stifled knell,
Alas! 'tis the sound of the eight o'clock bell.

Come, now we'll to bed! and when we are there
He may work his own will, and what shall we care?
He may knock at the door—we'll not let him in;
May drive at the windows—we'll laugh at his din.
Let him seek his own home, wherever it be:
Here's a cosy warm house for Edward and me.

Dorothy Wordsworth

SOUVENIR

I bring back a shell so I can always hear
the music of the ocean when I hold it to my ear:

then I feel again the grains of sand
trickle sun-warm through my hand

the sea gulls dip and swoop and cry
as they dive for fish then climb the sky

the sailboats race with wings spread wide
as the wind spins them round and they glide ride glide

my lips taste a crust of salty foam
and sandpipers skitter and crabs scuttle home

where I build a castle of Yesterday
that the high tide washed away away

while I keep the shell so I can always hear
the music of the ocean when I hold it to my ear.

David McCord

MY ANIMAL FRIENDS

"Bee! I'm expecting you!"

Bee! I'm expecting you!
Was saying yesterday
To somebody you know
That you were due.

The frogs got home last week,
Are settled, and at work;
Birds, mostly back,
The clover warm and thick.

You'll get my letter by
the seventeenth; reply
Or better, be with me,
Yours, Fly.

· *Emily Dickinson*

WHAT IS A BUTTERFLY?

What is a butterfly? At best
He's but a caterpillar dressed.

· *Anonymous*

FIREFLY

A Song

A little light is going by,
Is going up to see the sky,
A little light with wings.

I never could have thought of it,
To have a little bug all lit
And made to go on wings.

Elizabeth Madox Roberts

From: ADVENTURES OF ISABEL

Isabel met an enormous bear,
Isabel, Isabel, didn't care.
The bear was hungry, the bear was ravenous,
The bear's mouth was cruel and cavernous.
The bear said, Isabel, glad to meet you,
How do, Isabel, now I'll eat you!
Isabel, Isabel, didn't worry;
Isabel didn't scream or scurry.
She washed her hands and she straightened her hair up,
Then Isabel quietly ate the bear up.

Ogden Nash

CROCODEAR

Why
Can't I have a crocodile?
I've wanted one for quite a while.
Oh, I would take good care of him:
I'd fill the tub, so he could swim.
I'd also put in sand and rocks.
I'd knit him Nile-green crocosocks
(To wear or not, just as he chose).
I'd kiss him on his croconose.
I'd let him curl up on my lap
And take a little croconap,
Oh, he'd be crococozy here,
And I would call him Crocodear,
And he would teach me *cree,* and *cro*
(A language other kids don't know),
And then I'd soon speak Crocodilish.
Don't you think that would be stylish?

Gina Ruck-Pauquet
(translated from the German
by Doris Orgel)

55

THE SONG OF THE JELLICLES

Jellicle Cats come out tonight
Jellicle Cats come one come all;
 The Jellicle Moon is shining bright—
Jellicles come to the Jellicle Ball.

Jellicle Cats are black and white
Jellicle Cats are rather small;
Jellicle Cats are merry and bright,
And pleasant to hear when they caterwaul.
Jellicle Cats have bright black eyes;
They like to practice their airs and graces
And wait for the Jellicle Moon to rise.

Jellicle Cats develop slowly,
Jellicle Cats are not too big;
Jellicle Cats are roly-poly,
They know how to dance a gavotte and a jig.
Until the Jellicle Moon appears
They make their toilette and take their repose:
Jellicles wash behind their ears,
Jellicles dry between their toes.

Jellicle Cats are white and black,
Jellicle Cats are of moderate size;
Jellicles jump like a jumping-jack,
Jellicle Cats have moonlit eyes.
They're quiet enough in the afternoon,
Reserving their terpsichorean powers
To dance by the light of the Jellicle Moon.

Jellicle Cats are black and white,
Jellicle Cats (as I said) are small;
If it happens to be a stormy night
They will practice a caper or two in the hall.
If it happens the sun is shining bright
You would say they had nothing to do at all:
They are resting and saving themselves to be right
For the Jellicle Moon and the Jellicle Ball.

T. S. Eliot

UNDERSEA

Beneath the waters
 Green and cool
The mermaids keep
 A swimming school.

The oysters trot;
 The lobsters prance;
The dolphins come
 To join the dance.

But the jellyfish
 Who are rather small,
Can't seem to learn
 The steps at all.

Marchette Chute

DUCKS' DITTY

All along the backwater,
Through the rushes tall,
Ducks are a-dabbling,
Up tails all!

Ducks' tails, drakes' tails,
Yellow feet a-quiver,
Yellow bills all out of sight
busy in the river!

Slushy green undergrowth
Where the roach swim—
Here we keep our larder,
Cool and full and dim.

Every one for what he likes!
We like to be
Heads down, tails up,
Dabbling free!

High in the blue above
Swifts whirl and call—
We are down a-dabbling
Up tails all!

Kenneth Grahame

THE SEAL

How must it feel
to be
a
seal
and swish among the
ducks
and teal
and swim
a cool
Virginia Reel
right underneath
somebody's
keel?
Then
much
to
somebody's surprise
pop up your head
right out of sea
and blink your big blue baby eyes
and flap your fins
with glee?
And o what bliss
on summer days
what bliss it is to lie and laze
on a warm mudflat
in the sun
and *sunbathe*
just
like
anyone.
I think the seal
has
all
the
fun.

Conrad Aiken

TO BE A DUCK

It must be fun to be a duck
and row yourself around
And race with others nip and tuck
and make a quacky sound,
and dribble water through your beak,
and wear a jacket white and sleek,
and be too waterproof to leak.

It must be fun to float and float
around and in between,
and when you're tired of being a boat
to be a submarine
and chase the minnows and the fish,
or take off with a whirry swish
and be an airplane if you wish.

Aileen Fisher

WONDERING

"who knows if the moon's a balloon"

Will there really be a "Morning"?
Is there such a thing as "Day"?
Could I see it from the mountain
If I were as tall as they?

Has it feet like Water lilies?
Has it feathers like a Bird?
Is it brought from famous countries
Of which I have never heard?

Oh some Scholar! Oh some Sailor!
Oh some Wise Man from the skies!
Please to tell a little Pilgrim
Where the place called "Morning" lies!

Emily Dickinson

THE STAR

Twinkle, twinkle, little star,
How I wonder what you are!
Up above the world so high,
Like a diamond in the sky.

When the blazing sun is gone,
When he nothing shines upon,
Then you show your little light,
Twinkle, twinkle, all the night.

Then the traveller in the dark,
Thanks you for your tiny spark,
He could not see which way to go,
If you did not twinkle so.

In the dark blue sky you keep,
And often through my curtains peep,
For you never shut your eye,
Till the sun is in the sky.

As your bright and tiny spark,
Lights the traveller in the dark—
Though I know not what you are,
Twinkle, twinkle, little star.

Jane Taylor

THE WIND

I saw you toss the kites on high
And blow the birds about the sky;
And all around I heard you pass,
Like ladies' skirts across the grass—
   O wind, a-blowing all day long,
   O wind, that sings so loud a song!

I saw the different things you did,
But always you yourself you hid.
I felt you push, I heard you call,
I could not see yourself at all—
   O wind, a-blowing all day long,
   O wind, that sings so loud a song!

O you that are so strong and cold,
O blower, are you young or old?
Are you a beast of field and tree,
Or just a stronger child than me?
   O wind, a-blowing all day long,
   O wind, that sings so loud a song!

            Robert Louis Stevenson

Is it robin o'clock?
Is it five after wing?
Is it quarter to leaf?
Is it nearly time for spring?

Is it grass to eleven?
Is it flower to eight?
Is it half-past snowflake?
Do we still have to wait?

            Eve Merriam

BIRD TALK

"Think . . ." said the robin,
"Think . . ." said the jay,
sitting in the garden
talking one day.

"Think about people—
the way they grow:
they don't have feathers
at all, you know.

"They don't eat beetles,
they don't grow wings,
they don't like sitting
on wires and things."

"Think . . ." said the robin,
"Think . . ." said the jay.
"Aren't people funny
to be that way?"

Aileen Fisher

WHERE GO THE BOATS?

Dark brown is the river,
    Golden is the sand.
It flows along forever,
    With trees on either hand.

Green leaves a-floating,
    Castle of the foam,
Boats of mine a-boating—
    Where will all come home?

On goes the river
    And out past the mill,
Away down the valley,
    Away down the hill.

Away down the river,
    A hundred miles or more,
Other little children
    Shall bring my boats ashore.

Robert Louis Stevenson

WHAT IS RED?

Red is a sunset
Blazy and bright.
Red is a feeling brave
With all your might.
Red is a sunburn
Spot on your nose,
Sometimes red
Is a red, red rose.
Red squiggles out
When you cut your hand.
Red is a brick and
A rubber band.
Red is a hotness
You get inside
When you're embarrassed
And want to hide.
Fire-cracker, fire-engine
Fire-flicker red—

And when you're angry
Red runs through your head.
Red is an Indian
A valentine heart,
The trimming on
A circus cart.
Red is a lipstick,
Red is a shout,
Red is a signal
That says: "Watch out!"
Red is a great big
Rubber ball.
Red is the giant-est
Color of all.
Red is a show-off
No doubt about it—
But can you imagine
Living without it?

Mary O'Neill

SKYSCRAPERS

Do skyscrapers ever grow tired
Of holding themselves up high?
Do they ever shiver on frosty nights
With their tops against the sky?
Do they feel lonely sometimes
Because they have grown so tall?
Do they ever wish they could lie right down
And never get up at all?

Rachel Field

BUNDLES

A bundle is a funny thing,
It always sets me wondering;
For whether it is thin or wide
You never know just what's inside.

Especially on Christmas week,
Temptation is so great to peek!
Now wouldn't it be much more fun
If shoppers carried things undone?

John Farrar

who knows if the moon's
a balloon, coming out of a keen city
in the sky—filled with pretty people?
(and if you and i should

get into it, if they
should take me and take you into their balloon,
why then
we'd go up higher with all the pretty people

than houses and steeples and clouds:
go sailing
away and away sailing into a keen
city which nobody's ever visited, where

always

  it's

    Spring) and everyone's
in love and flowers pick themselves

e. e. cummings